784.4
Bra
c.5 Brand, Oscar
 AUTHOR

Singing Holidays
 TITLE

784.4   Brand, Oscar
Bra   Singing Holidays   8785
c. 5

SINGING HOLIDAYS

The Calendar

IN

Folk Song

SINGING HOLIDAYS

The Calendar in Folk Song

BY

OSCAR BRAND

MUSICAL ARRANGEMENTS BY
DOUGLAS TOWNSEND

ILLUSTRATED BY ROBERTA MOYNIHAN

New York 〜 *Alfred A. Knopf*

L. C. catalog card number: 57-5253

© OSCAR BRAND, 1957

THIS IS A BORZOI BOOK,
PUBLISHED BY ALFRED A. KNOPF, INC.

For Rubyann, my wife

INTRODUCTION

The Songs

When the first immigrants landed in America, they carried with them seeds for planting, sewing utensils for making clothes, hand tools for building, and folk songs to keep up their spirits.

They had no radio, television, or motion pictures. The folk song was their newspaper, their entertainment, and their way of commenting on their daily lives. As their daily lives changed, they found it necessary to add new verses to the old songs.

But, in a completely new world, a patchwork song isn't enough. Completely new songs had to be made up about war, disaster, romance, and outlawry. These new songs were sung by ear, learned by heart, and passed on through the process known as "the oral tradition."

Among our holiday folk songs are patchwork songs, completely new songs, and songs that were old when Columbus first landed on our continent. It would be a pity if these songs stopped changing just because they were written down in this book. Therefore, if you feel like adding a new verse, or putting your own name in a song, go right ahead. And if you don't like the melody, make up your own.

Let's go even further. If you want a song that says something different, write it yourself. Use an old melody if you wish, or make up a new one. And if someone says, sneeringly, "That's a very familiar tune," just keep singing. If the tune is familiar enough, that "someone" will soon be singing along.

We've chosen thirty dates in the busy American year; we've illustrated these with some ninety appropriate folk songs. It is our hope that when Washington's Birthday comes along, a song about his ragged army may help bring the exciting days of the Revolution to life.

We would have liked to do the same service for Columbus Day. Not knowing the songs of Columbus's sailors, we included some songs *about* Columbus. And for good measure, we added an old sea song that was a favorite in the days of the Spanish Armada.

I have recorded many of the melodies in this book for Young People's Records' "The American Almanac," and for The Children's Record Guild, but you needn't try copying my way of singing. Your way is best for you.

All these songs are "game" songs. If there is no traditional dance or game that is noted in the introduction, don't hesitate to make up one. That's how many of our "play-party" songs got to be games.

If you just want to sing the songs for fun, or for artistic expression, please do.

OSCAR BRAND

The Arrangements

BEFORE arranging the songs in this collection, it was necessary to write them down as Mr. Brand sang them. This task was not always a simple one, since Mr. Brand would one day sing a song one way, and the following day in a completely different way.

The music arranger, like the linguist, translates from one language into another. Apart from the mechanical question of choosing keys for the songs, it was necessary to decide not only how complex the piano part should be, but what harmonic idiom (or musical language) was to be used. Since most of the songs are simple and direct, I decided to arrange them in a musical idiom which would be simple and direct, even at the risk of being called a musical conservative or reactionary by my colleagues. However, in "The Bold Fisherman," the humor of the song lies not only in the words, but in the changes in time signature. In setting this song I have kept the harmony simple, but followed the basic waltz pattern in the left hand. This means that in the chorus, the left hand always plays a waltz-like accompaniment while the right hand plays the tune with all its vagaries of changing meter.

Three of the songs in this collection were harmonized by others. My reason for using these arrangements, rather than my own, is simple. There is a degree of intensity in them which in my opinion can't quite be matched by a contemporary composer. The songs are: 1) "A Happy New Year," the harmonization of which appears in a seventeenth century volume of lute music called *The Lute Book* of William Ballet. 2) "In Freedom We're Born," originally "Hearts of Oak," composed by William

Boyce, an early and middle eighteenth century composer (see Mr. Brand's note in the text). After consulting a number of slightly different versions of this song, I have given what seemed in my opinion the harmonization most nearly approximating the original. 3) "Hail Columbia," in the setting of James Hewitt, an American composer and contemporary of Beethoven's. The piano part has been prepared so that it can be performed either as a song or as "The President's March," on which it is based. The small notes in the piano part refer to the original march *only*.

Many of the songs in this collection may be used as piano pieces for adult beginners. To this end I have suggested fingerings for those passages which I felt might cause some difficulty.

This introduction would not be complete without a word of thanks to Arnold Broido for his many excellent suggestions regarding the arrangements, for proofreading, and for other details involved in producing this book. To Milton Feist thanks are also in order for his advice and many helpful suggestions.

DOUGLAS TOWNSEND

Acknowledgments

WE ARE indebted to many singers and collectors for the songs we've listed in our holiday book. Some of the songs were first taught to me by people whose names have been long forgotten. Some of the verses were traded to me, free and clear, in exchange for verses that I alone knew.

Sometimes, in performing for an audience, I have joined other singers in making up new verses. It's often impossible to ascertain where my contribution ends and theirs begins. In a few instances, I heard other singers perform songs which I coveted. I admit that I often appropriated their songs for my own audience.

For that reason, some of the people on this "acknowledgment list" will be surprised to find their names among the many: Paddy and Tom Clancy of Ireland, Isla Cameron of England, Tom Glazer, Hamish Henderson of Scotland, Burl Ives, Huddie Ledbetter, Alan Lomax, Ed McCurdy, Brownie McGhee, Robin Roberts, Peter Seeger, Frank Warner, Josh White, and Hally Wood.

I would especially like to thank Jean Ritchie of Kentucky and her husband, George Pickow, for singing around with me in America, Ireland, England, Scotland, Germany, France, Holland, Belgium, and Luxemburg.

I would like to thank the fellow soldiers who filled my barracks with songs during my three years in World War II. I'd also like to thank the migrant workers, the farm hands, and the country dancers who traded verses with me for so many years.

While I was broadcasting for New York City's Municipal Radio Station, many listeners contributed songs and verses which have found their way onto these pages. I would like to thank those listeners and the men who kept my program on the air: Seymour N. Siegel, Director of Communications for the City of New York; Hermann Neuman, Musical Director; the many program directors, including the incumbent, Bernard Buck; and, of course, the men who held the office of Mayor during the eleven years of broadcasting—Fiorello H. La Guardia, William O'Dwyer, Vincent R. Impelliteri, and Robert F. Wagner.

Finally, we are extremely grateful to William Cole for his suggestions, and to Milton Feist for his invaluable advice in the organization of the musical portion of the book.

OSCAR BRAND

CONTENTS

Contents

Contents

NEW YEAR'S DAY

January 1

⮑§ THE ROMANS named January for their god, Janus. Janus had two faces—one looking forward into the future, and one looking back into the past. On New Year's Day, we look forward with hope for a happy year, and we look back, over our shoulders, at the days gone by. Of course, unlike Janus, we do the whole thing with only one face.

IN AMERICA, on New Year's Day, practically everyone sings "Auld Lang Syne," a song that we borrowed from Scotland. The song reminds us that no one is ever really alone. And, on the threshold of the new year, it reminds us to think of our friends, our family, and our faith, for "Old Time's Sake"—for "Auld Lang Syne."

Auld Lang Syne

days of auld lang syne? For auld lang syne, my dear, For auld lang
auld lang syne.

syne, We'll take a cup of kind - ness yet, For auld lang syne.

ONE OF THE oldest melodies sung by English-speaking people is called "Greensleeves." It has been used as a tune for all sorts of songs, from hymns to low comedy dances. In 1642, there appeared a collection of carols, one of which used the melody of "Greensleeves" for a New Year's song. Today, in New England, there are versions of this old carol which can still be heard if one asks the proper question of the proper people.

A Happy New Year

1. The old year now does pass a - way, The New Year comes a -
joy - ous greet - ings now we send, With heart and hand to

while to stay, So let us mer - ry be this day And sing with joy - ful cheer.
ev - 'ry friend, And pray we may our lives a - mend, And good deeds soon ap - pear.

Let joy be un-con-fin'd, Put grief and sor-row far be-hind,
Now, let us wel-come in The good-ly days that soon be-gin,

Fare-well to a trou-bled mind, And send us a hap-py New Year. 2. Our
Cast off all thoughts of sin, And send us a hap-py New Year.

"WASSAIL" COMES FROM two words in the old Anglo-Saxon language—"Wes Hal," which means "Good Health." On New Year's Day, the carolers would walk through the snow and stand outside the windows of the brightly lit houses and sing songs of good cheer for the people who looked out through the frosted panes. Sometimes, the singers were invited in for dinner. Sometimes, they were given a few pennies as good luck tokens.

The Wassail Song

you, and to you your was-sail, too, And God bless you and send ___ you a

hap - py New Year, And God send you a hap - py New Year.

1. 𝅗𝅥. = 𝅗𝅥   last time

2. God
3. We
4. The

5. To all your kin and kindred That live both far and near,
We wish a Merry Christmas And a happy New Year.

LINCOLN'S BIRTHDAY

February 12

ABRAHAM LINCOLN was born on February 12, 1809, in a back-woods section of Kentucky known as "Sinking Springs." The Americans who lived near the frontier in those days had very little time for vacations or for games, but Lincoln managed to learn many of the old songs and play-party dances. Unlike many adults who forget the fun of being young, Lincoln never hesitated to sing a verse of an old song when it came to his mind, or to quote an old joke when the situation called for humor.

❧ WHEN ABRAHAM LINCOLN was our sixteenth President, he went to speak at Gettysburg, Pennsylvania. The Grand Marshal in charge of the opening of the new Civil War Monument was Ward Lamon, Lincoln's old friend. It is said that Lincoln asked Ward Lamon, who was a very good banjo picker, to play and sing for him the funny little plantation song about "The Blue Tail Fly."

The Blue Tail Fly

Chorus ♩=80 (Gaily)

brush a-way the blue tail fly.
bit-ten by the blue tail fly.
dev-il take the blue tail fly.
ver-dict was, "The blue tail fly."

Jim-my crack corn, but I don't care,

Jim-my crack corn, but I don't care, Jim-my crack corn, but I don't care, My

mas-ter's gone a-way. 2. And
3. One
4. The way.

5. They laid him under the 'simmons tree,
His epitaph for all to see:
"Beneath this stone I'm forced to lie,
The victim of the blue tail fly."
CHORUS

6. My master's gone, so let him rest,
They say such things are for the best.
But I won't forget till the day I die
My master and the blue tail fly.
CHORUS

WHEN ABRAHAM LINCOLN was a candidate for the presidency in 1860, his followers made up many campaign songs by writing new words to well known melodies. When the campaign was over and the election was won, most of these songs disappeared. But one of them, written to the tune of "The Old Gray Mare," kept singing around. Even today, it can be heard in widely separated sections of the nation.

Old Abe Lincoln

1. Old Abe Lin-coln, he came out of the wil-der-ness,
2. Old Abe Lin-coln, he moved in-to the White House,
3. Old Jeff Dav-is, he tore down the gov-ern-ment,
4. Old Abe Lin-coln, he built it right up a-gain,

Out of the wil-der-ness, out of the wil-der-ness; Old Abe Lin-coln, he came
In-to the White House, in-to the White House; Old Abe Lin-coln, he moved
Tore down the gov-ern-ment, tore down the gov-ern-ment; Old Jeff Dav-is, he
Built it right up a-gain, built it right up a-gain; Old Abe Lin-coln, he

out of   the wil-der-ness, Down in   Il -   li - nois.
in- to   the White House, Man-y long years a - go.
tore down   the gov-ern-ment, Man-y long years a - go.
built it   right up a- gain, Man-y long years a - go.

last time

f

[13]

ABRAHAM LINCOLN lived in many states before he settled down in the White House in Washington, D. C. He was born in Kentucky, but his family later moved to Indiana. Eventually he opened a law office in Illinois, then known as "The Sucker State" because of the great number of sucker fish in local streams. In an effort to help their candidate, Lincoln's supporters rewrote Henry Clay's campaign song and used it to help elect "Honest Abe." This wasn't as unfair as it might seem, since Henry Clay's song writers had taken the melody from the old Irish favorite, "Rosin the Beau."

Lincoln and Liberty

rah for the choice of the na-tion,— Our chief-tain so brave and so
find what by fel-ling and maul-ing,— Our rail-split-ter states-man can
Da- vid's good sling is un- er-ring,— The Slav- o- crat's gi- ant he

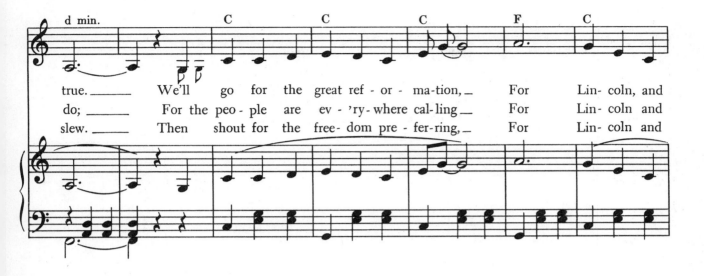

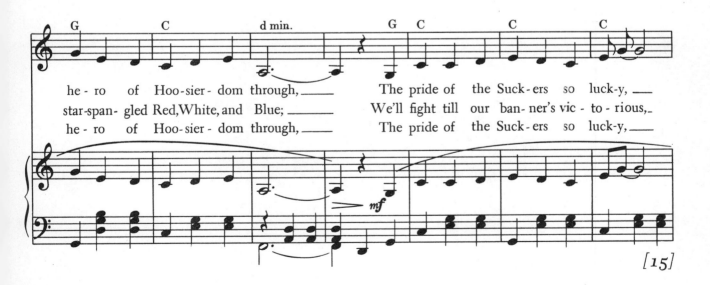

For ___ Lin - coln and lib - er - ty, too. ___
For ___ Lin - coln and lib - er - ty, too. ___
For ___ Lin - coln and lib - er - ty, too. ___

2. They'll
3. Our

*⤙ LINCOLN HAD two sons, Tad and Robert, but when the Union soldiers marched into battle they sang about "Abraham's Daughter." The song explains, however, that they were singing about the Union, and about Lincoln as the Father of the American Constitution.

The uniform of the American soldier wasn't as uniform as it is today. Some of the costumes were very colorful and somewhat strange. For instance, the "Fire Zou-Zous" wore bizarre dress uniforms with African trimmings. Nevertheless, in battle, the soldiers all wore Union Blue.

Abraham's Daughter

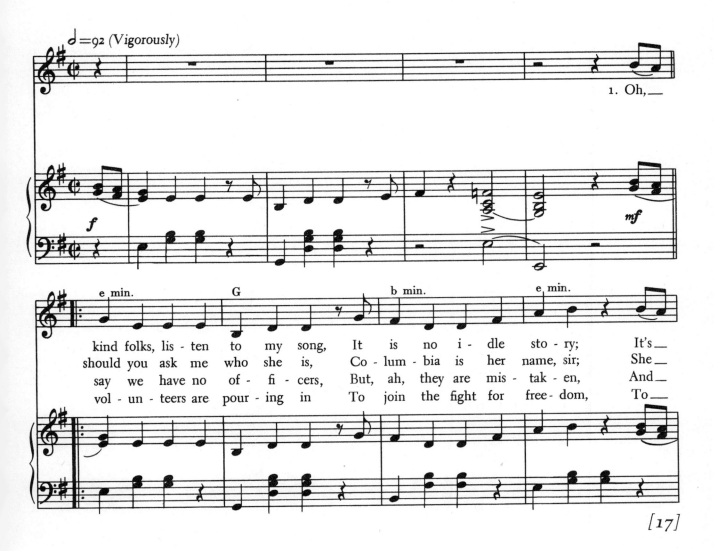

kind folks, lis - ten to my song, It is no i - dle sto - ry; It's __
should you ask me who she is, Co - lum - bia is her name, sir; She __
say we have no of - fi - cers, But, ah, they are mis - tak - en, And __
vol - un - teers are pour - ing in To join the fight for free - dom, To __

all a-bout a vol-un-teer Who's going to fight _ for _ glo - ry. Now,
is the child of A - bra - ham, Of Un - cle Sam, _ the _ same, sir; And
soon you'll see the reb- els run With all the fuss _ he's _ mak - in'. Mc -
swell the ranks of Un - ion blue, And noth- ing now _ can _ beat 'em. One

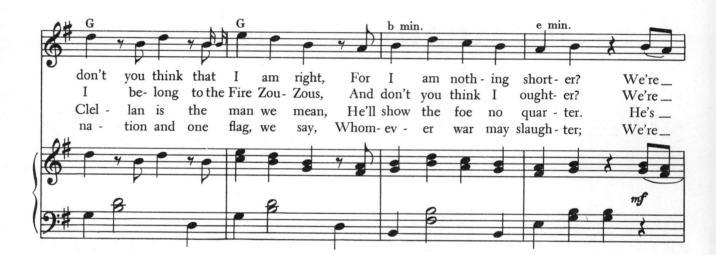

don't you think that I am right, For I am noth- ing short- er? We're _
I be- long to the Fire Zou- Zous, And don't you think I ought- er? We're _
Clel- lan is the man we mean, He'll show the foe no quar- ter. He's _
na - tion and one flag, we say, Whom- ev- er war may slaugh- ter; We're _

go - ing down to Wash - ing- town to fight for A-bra- ham's _ daugh - ter.
go - ing down to Vicks - burg town to fight for A-bra- ham's _ daugh - ter.
go - ing down to Rich - mond town to fight for A-bra- ham's _ daugh - ter.
go - ing down to Charles- ton town to fight for A-bra- ham's _ daugh - ter.

[18]

SAINT VALENTINE'S DAY

February 14

IN ENGLAND, many years ago, it was believed that the wild birds of the forest chose their mates at this time of the year. The old singers thought it would be pleasant to keep this day for exchanging love songs and affectionate greetings. The ancient Romans had a custom for this time of the year which is still observed in some parts of our country. They would put the names of the young men in a box and have the young women pick them out blindfolded. This, however, is too haphazard a method for picking a sweetheart.

OUR FIRST SONG for Saint Valentine's Day is one of the best-known in this country. It's sung in so many different ways that it would fill this book and many others if we tried to print even a few of the different versions. Experts say that "My Boy Billy" comes from the very sad ballad, "Lord Randall," but the version we like the best isn't the least bit sad.

My Boy Billy

♩ = 100-104 (Lightly)

1. Where have you been all the day, My boy Bil-ly? Where have you been all the day, Bil-ly, won't you tell me now?
2. Can she bake and can she brew, My boy Bil-ly? Can she bake and can she brew, Bil-ly, won't you tell me now?
3. Can she make up a bed, My boy Bil-ly? Can she make up a bed, Bil-ly, won't you tell me now?
4. Can she cook a plate of fish, My boy Bil-ly? Can she cook a plate of fish, Bil-ly, won't you tell me now?

I have been all the day Court - ing with my la - dy gay. ___
She can brew, she can bake, She can make a wed - ding cake. ___
She can make up a bed Fif - ty feet a - bove her head. ___
She can cook a plate of fish With her fin - gers in the dish. ___

But she is too young to be tak - en from her mam - my, But she is too young to be tak - en from her mam - my.

last time only

5. Can she sew and can she spin, My boy Billy?
   Can she sew and can she spin, Billy, won't you tell me now?
   She can sew and she can spin, She can do most anythin'.
   CHORUS

6. How old can she be, My boy Billy?
   How old can she be, Billy, Won't you tell me now?
   She is two, she is seven, She is twenty-and-eleven.
   CHORUS

7. Did you ask her to wed, My boy Billy?
   Did you ask her to wed, Billy, won't you tell me now?
   Yes, I asked her to wed, And these are the words she said:
   CHORUS: "I am much too young to be taken from my mammy,
   I am much too young to be taken from my mammy."

SAINT VALENTINE'S DAY parties often feature games in which the young people choose partners while singing "choosing-out" songs. In this play-party song, a young man and a young lady sit in the center of a ring of boys. When the "father" in the center picks one of the boys in the ring, that boy takes one of the girls who is watching the game and dances with her. Then he brings her to the center of the ring to take the place of the girl who was playing the "daughter."

Hog Drovers

♩·=60 (Waltz time)

1. Hog dro - vers, hog dro - vers, hog
   have but one daugh- ter who
   care not for your daugh- ter and
   have but one daugh- ter, she

dro - vers we are, A - court - ing your daugh - ter so young and so fair; And
sits by my side, And_ none of you dro - vers may have her to bride; And
less for your - self, We'll_ trav - el on fur - ther and bet - ter our wealth; And
sits by my knee, And_ one of you dro - vers can get her from me, By

can we find lodg - ing here, __ oh, __ here, And can we find lodg - ing
you can't find lodg - ing here, __ oh, __ here, And you can't find lodg - ing
we won't take lodg - ing here, __ oh, __ here, And we won't take lodg - ing
bring - ing an - oth - er one here, __ oh, __ here, By bring - ing an - oth - er one

1.   last time

here? _____   2. I
here. _____   3. We
here. _____   4. I
here. _____

(When all girls but one are chosen, "Father" sings this verse:)

5. I have no more daughters excepting this one,
   I'll take her myself and now there will be none;
   And you bring another one here, oh, here,
   And you bring another one here.

(Another "Father" is chosen and the game continues.)

[25]

⊷§ CANTERBURY CATHEDRAL is one of the most impressive buildings in the world. For centuries, pilgrims have come to worship under the great arches that thrust high up toward the heavens. In this song, the young man offers the young lady the keys to the cathedral if she will marry him. Of course, he doesn't own Canterbury, nor can he make all the bells in London ring. But she does accept him when he offers her the one gift which is perfect for Saint Valentine's Day.

The Keys of Canterbury

3. HE: Madame, I will give to you a dress of silken red,
 Stitched all around with a gold and silver thread,
  If you will be, &c.

3a. SHE: Sir, I'll not accept of you a dress of silken red,
 Stitched all around with a gold and silver thread,
  And I'll not be, &c.

4. HE: Madame, I will give to you the keys of my heart,
 And all my solemn promises that we will never part,
  If you will be, &c.

4a. SHE: Sir, I will accept of you the keys to your heart,
 And all your solemn promises that we will never part,
  And I will be your darling, your joy, and your dear,
  And I will go a-walking with you everywhere.

ONE OF THE oldest legends known to man is the story of the riddle of the Sphinx. It is said that this monster destroyed all passers-by who couldn't answer the riddle, "What travels on four's in the morning, on two's in the afternoon, and on three's in the evening?" The great king Oedipus answered, "Man crawls on four's in the morning of his life, walks on two's in the afternoon of his life, and using a cane, travels on three's in the evening of his life." Riddles are among the earliest games and songs, and this is one of the many in which love is the subject.

I Will Give My Love an Apple

♩=80 (Flowing)

1. I will give my love an ap - ple with - out_ an - y
   can there be an ap - ple with - out_ an - y
   head is an_ ap - ple with - out_ an - y

core, I will give my love a house_ with - out_ an - y door, I will
core? How_ can there be a house_ with - out an - y door? How_
core, My_ mind is the house_ with - out an - y door, My_

[28]

give my love a pal - ace where - in __ she may be, And __ she may un -
can there be a pal - ace where - in __ she may be, And __ she may un -
heart is the __ pal - ace where - in __ she may be, And __ she may un -

lock it with - out an - y key.
lock it with - out an - y key?
lock it with - out an - y key.

2. How
3. My

WASHINGTON'S BIRTHDAY

February 22

GEORGE WASHINGTON was born in Virginia in 1732. His ancestral estate was named Mount Vernon after a British Admiral who was a good friend of the family. The Admiral made plans to enter George as a midshipman in a British naval training school, but Mrs. Washington put a stop to it. And so George Washington, like many young men, was given military training, and became a major at the beginning of the French and Indian War. His bravery under fire and his wisdom in commanding troops made him a commander-in-chief of the Virginia militia at the age of twenty-three.

GEORGE WASHINGTON wasn't the dramatic, dashing leader that is usually expected in revolutionary eras. He was a simple, quiet-spoken man. But the dramatic, dashing leaders of the American Revolution decided that a simple, quiet-spoken man would make the best commander-in-chief. Besides, they wanted a southerner to lead the troops in order to convince the southern states that this wasn't merely a New England enterprise. The troops, however, didn't ask questions when Washington took command. They knew he was an efficient officer, and they followed him wherever he led.

Follow Washington

he that leads the way.   2. Where
ter- mined to   be   free.   3. Till
til our cause pre - vails.   4. With
fol - low Wash - ing -   ton.

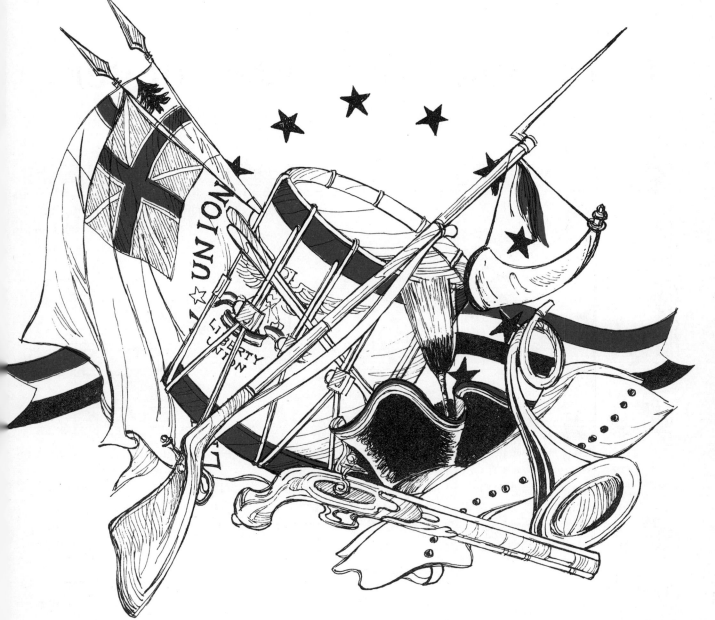

GEORGE WASHINGTON never wanted to be commander-in-chief. He refused a salary, explaining that he didn't feel worthy of the honor, nor deserving of pay. His first task was to arrange for equipment and to train the new army. The ragged soldiers were told that there were two types of commands, "preparatory" which warned them to get ready, and "commands of execution," which called forth the desired action. Sometimes the "command of execution" sounded more like a bark than a word, but, after a while, the soldiers caught on.

Come Out, Ye Continentalers

♩=92 (Pompously)

1. Come out, ye Continentalers, we're going for to go,— To fight the red-coat
2. First, shoulder WHOOP, eyes right and DRESS FRONT, don't you twitch your nose;— Port, WHOOP, that's good, now
3. Now bayonet FIX, that's fine, my men, Now quick-time, MARCH, that's right;— That's how we'd poke the
4. HALT, shoulder WHOOP, stop laughing there, By columns, WHEEL, HALT, DRESS;— Hold up your muzzles

sempre stacc.

en - em - y, Who's pla - guy cute, you know, my boys, Who's pla - guy cute, you know.
car - ry, WHOOP, Now all turn in your toes, my boys, Now all turn in your toes.
en - em - y, If he were but in sight, my men, If he were but in sight.
on the left, No talk- ing, more or less, my men, No talk- ing, more or less.

5. Ho, strike up MUSIC, forward MARCH,
   The red-coats are in sight.
   Now, bayonets FIX, and CHARGE, my men,
   We'll show them how we fight, my men,
   We'll show them how we fight.

AT FIRST, the campaign went badly. Many Americans conspired against the Revolution, believing that the Colonies were better off under the British flag. It was hard to collect taxes, and the new army had practically no supplies. But honest, loyal men began to join Washington's forces. Among them was Richard Boyle, an Englishman who came to America in 1778, enlisted as a volunteer and composed the following song. The last verse may have been written with General Washington in mind.

The Bold Volunteer

1. Here's to the squire ___ that goes on pa - rade,
2. Here's to the law - yer, who leav-ing the bar
3. Here's to the farm - er who dares to ad - vance To
4. Here's to the sol - dier, though bat-tered in wars, And

Here's to the cit - i - zen sol - dier; ___ Here's to the mer - chant who
Has - tens where hon - or doth lead, sir, ___ Chang - ing his gown for the
har - vests of hon - or, with pleas - ure, ___ Who, brave - ly, with dan - ger will
safe to his farm - house re - tired; ___ When called by his coun - try, ne'er

fights for his trade, Whom dan-ger in-creas-ing makes bold-er._____
en-sign of war, The cause of his coun-try to plead, sir._____
ven-ture a chance, A sword for his coun-try to meas-ure._____
thinks of his scars, With ar-dor to join us in-spired._____

Chorus

Let mirth ap-pear, ev-'ry heart cheer, Here's health and suc-cess to the bold vol-un-

teer.

SAINT PATRICK'S DAY

March 17

◈ EXCEPT FOR the Indian, our country is made up of Americans of foreign descent. Sometimes these Americans use their old country celebrations to demonstrate their contribution to our national culture. The Polish-Americans celebrate Pulaski Day, the Greeks and the Russians have their own New Year's and Easter holidays, the Scottish-Americans feast on St. Andrew's Day, and the Irish-Americans parade on March 17th. For this collection, St. Patrick's Day will serve to honor all the people who helped build our country.

IRISH SETTLERS first began coming to America before the Revolution. But the great tide of Irish immigration arrived just in time to help build the canals and railroads that unified our nation. The railroad work gangs used to sing this song in chorus, as they moved the rails, hammered down the spikes, and levered the wooden ties into place.

Pat Works on the Railway

1. In eight - een hun - dred for - ty - one, I put my cord - 'roy britch - es on; I put my cord - 'roy
2. In eight - een hun - dred for - ty - two, I left the old world for the new; Bad luck to the boat that
3. In eight - een hun - dred for - ty - three, I took the boat a - cross the sea; To find at last a
4. 'Twas "Pat do this," and "Pat do that," With - out a stock - ing or cra - vat, Sure, noth - ing but an

5. In eighteen hundred forty-six,
   Says I, "I'm in an awful fix."
   I changed my trade to carrying bricks,
   From working on the railway.
   CHORUS

There was a time when any citizen could go out to the western plains and own the land he farmed—if he farmed it for five years and paid a small fee to the government. The growing young nation needed the help of all the people it could get. Government agents encouraged immigrants to travel out to the West, and this song played its part in convincing the newcomers to take up the farming life.

Uncle Sam's Farm

♩=112 (Lively-Vigorously)

1. Of __
2. Saint __

D · D · D · A

all the might-y na-tions in the east and in the west, Our ____
room for all cre- a- tion and our ban- ner is un- furled, With a
Law-rence marks our north-ern line, as fast her wa- ter flows; And the
great Pa- ci- fic O- cean where the sun be- gins to dawn, Leap a-

glo - rious Yan - kee na - tion is the great - est and the best; We have
gen - 'ral in - vi - ta - tion to the peo - ple of the
Ri - o Grande our south - ern bounds, way down to Mex - i - co. From the
cross the Rock - y Moun - tains far a - way to Or - e -

world.
gon. So, come a - long, come a - long, come ___ when you can,

Come from ev - 'ry na - tion, come from ev - 'ry land;

[43]

Our land is large e-nough, don't ___ be a-larmed, For ___
Un-cle Sam is rich e-nough to give us all a farm.

3. While the South shall raise the cotton,
   And the West the corn and pork,
   The New England manufactories shall do the finer work;
   For the deep and flowing waterfalls
   That course along our hills
   Are just the thing for washing sheep
   And driving cotton mills.
   CHORUS

The Wayfaring Stranger

1. I'm just a poor _____ way-far-ing stran-ger, _____ Trav'-ling
2. I'll soon be cured _____ of ev-ery tri-al, _____ My bod-y a-
3. My fa-ther lived _____ and died a farm-er, _____ A-reap-ing
4. Our fa-thers came _____ a-cross the o-cean _____ To found this

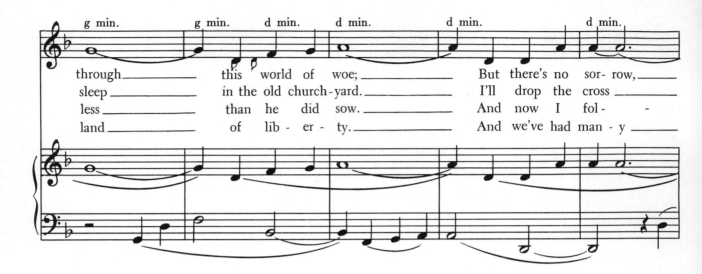

through_____ this world of woe;_____ But there's no sor- row,_____
sleep_____ in the old church-yard._____ I'll drop the cross_____
less_____ than he did sow._____ And now I fol - -
land_____ of lib - er - ty._____ And we've had man - y _____

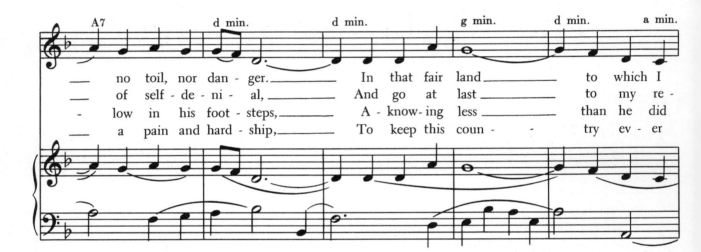

__ no toil, nor dan - ger._____ In that fair land_____ to which I
__ of self - de - ni - al,_____ And go at last_____ to my re-
- low in his foot - steps,_____ A - know-ing less_____ than he did
__ a pain and hard - ship,_____ To keep this coun - - try ev - er

Chorus

go._____
ward._____ I'm go - ing there _____ to see my fa - ther,_____
know._____
free._____

I'm go-ing there, _____ no more to roam; _____ I'm on-ly

go - - - ing o-ver Jor - dan, _____ I'm on-ly

go - - - ing to my home. _____

SPRING

 EVERY YEAR, just when we've had enough winter, spring arrives. This season begins when the night and the day are of equal length. Then, according to old songs and legends, wonderful things happen very suddenly. The birds appear in the northern regions, the flowers burst into view, and young men and young women fall in love automatically.

🙢 IT IS DOUBTFUL that all the wonderful things for which spring is known happen on just one day. But it's fun to think of spring as the sudden signal for gaiety and as a cue for all growing things to spring into being after the cold austerity of winter. In our first song, a cowboy rides among the signs of springtime and thinks of other things besides cows.

It Is Spring

1. It ___ is spring, the dai - sies are bust - ing out; It ___ is spring, the grass ___ is
2. Me and my horse go clip - pet - y clop - pet - y, Me and my horse go jig - get - y
3. I ___ just left the Doub - le - X Ranch, ___ I got on my horse and rode ___ a -

ten - der, And the ___ breeze is blow - ing so soft - ly,
jog - get - y, As we go rid - ing, clip - pet - y clop - pet - y,
way. ____ I know a pret - ty girl lives in the val - ley,

last time

O - ver the rol - ling plains.
O - ver the rol - ling plains.
O - ver the rol - ling plains.

⤳ MANY OF OUR favorite birds stay with us the year around. Still, the legend persists that all the birds go south for the winter and are never seen again until spring. The cuckoo, especially, has been called "the messenger of spring." It was also believed, in the old days, that the cuckoo could foretell the future. But in this British-American song, the cuckoo is ascribed no magic power at all—just the inability to sing a note until the spring season arrives.

The Cuckoo

1. The cuck - oo is a fun - ny bird, She sings as she flies. She'll bring you glad ___ tid - ings, She'll tell you no
   walk - ing and a - talk - ing, And a - wan - d'ring go I, A - wait - ing for my true ___ love; He'll come by and
   all you fair ___ maid - ens, Take warn - ing from me Don't place your af - fec - tions On a young man too
   if he will ___ leave ___ me, I'll not be for - lorn; And if he'll for - swear ___ me, I'll not be for -

lies. She sips from the pret-ty flow-ers To make her voice clear, And she'll
by. I'll meet him in the morn-ing, For he's all my de-light. I could
free; For leaves, they do with-er, And roots they do die, And your
sworn; I'll get my-self up in My best fin-er-y, And I'll

mf   *mp*

nev-er sing, "Cuck-oo," Till the spring of the year. 2. A-
walk with my true love From morn-ing to night. 3. Come,
love he will leave you And he'll nev-er say why. 4. But
walk as proud by him, As he walks by me.

[53]

ONE OF OUR favorite Christmas carols, "Good King Wenceslaus," owes much of its popularity to its very lilting melody. But that melody originally belonged to an old spring carol, which was a favorite in the sixteenth century. Here is the old spring carol, which tells how time has brought the flowers back to life.

Spring Carol

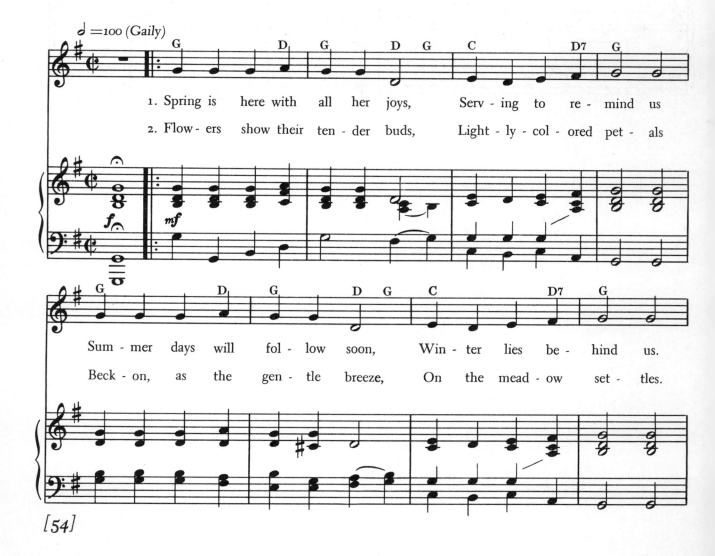

1. Spring is here with all her joys, Serv-ing to re-mind us
2. Flow-ers show their ten-der buds, Light-ly-col-ored pet-als

Sum-mer days will fol-low soon, Win-ter lies be-hind us.
Beck-on, as the gen-tle breeze, On the mead-ow set-tles.

Snow has melt - ed fast a - way, All the earth is warm - ing.
Warm and hap - py in the sun, Na - ture shows her treas - ures;

Birds are fly - ing from the south, In - sect life is swarm - ing.
All the world has come a - wake, Wait - ing spring - time pleas - ures.

ALL FOOLS' DAY

April 1

ON ALL FOOLS' DAY, practical jokers declare an open season on innocent victims, and organize all sorts of unfair tricks. In Scotland this is called "Hunting the Gowk." In France, they call it "Fooling the April Fish." As far as we're concerned, there are more pleasant ways to celebrate April 1st. Our favorite is the singing of foolish songs in which everyone can participate without the fear of ridicule.

ONCE UPON A TIME there lived a great philosopher who maintained, "I think; therefore, I am." Often, if we think at all, we wonder who we are and what we're doing on the earth. The old lady in this song was foolish enough to believe that her dog was the only authority on the subject of her identity. Without question, she was an April 1st "Fish." And the mean pedlar who played a practical joke on her was, as far as we're concerned, an April "Gowk."

There Was an Old Lady

went to the mar-ket, as I've heard say, fa - la, fa la - la, fa - la - la. And she
cut her pet-ti-coats up to her knees, fa - la, fa - la - la, fa - la - la, Which ___

fell a - sleep on the King's High - way, fa - la - la, fa - la - la, fa - la - la
made the old la - dy to shiv-er and sneeze, fa - la - la, fa - la - la, fa - la -

1.   last time

la. _____
la. _____

2. There
3. Then the
4. "But
5. Then

D.S. al 𝄋

3. Then the little old lady began to awake, falala, falala, falala.
   She began to shiver, she began to shake, falala, falala, falala.
   She began to shake, she began to cry, fala, falala, falala.
   "Oh, dearie me, this is none of I," falala, falala, falala.

4. "But if it be me, as I hope it be," falala, falala, falala,
   "I've a doggie at home, and I know he knows me," falala, falala, falala.
   "And if it be I, he will wag his tail," fala, falala, falala.
   "And if it be not, he will bark and he'll wail," falala, falala, falala.

5. Then home went the old lady, all in the dark, falala, falala, falala.
   Up rose her dog and he started to bark, falala, falala, falala.
   He started to bark, and she started to cry, fala, falala, falala,
   "Oh, dearie me, this is none of I," falala, falala, falala.

[59]

AMERICANS ARE supposed to be especially skilled at telling "tall tales," like the one about the man who was so tall he had to climb a ladder to shave himself. This song, about a remarkable ram, came to us many years ago with the English settlers who were also skilled at storytelling. We include this song as an April 1st selection, but it's just as much fun when sung in May.

The Darby Ram

ev - er fed on hay.
make his wife a gown.
nev - er come down till June.
heard the young ones cry.

Chorus ♩=112 (With gusto)

And did - n't he ram - ble,

e min.

ram - ble? He ram-bled till the but-cher cut him down.

1. G

last time G

2. This
3. This down.
4. The

FIVE BLIND MEN were examining an elephant. One, who touched the trunk, said an elephant was like a snake. Another leaned on the elephant's side and claimed the creature was like a wall. The third, feeling the leg, said it was like a tree. The fourth swore the elephant was more like a whip; he was holding the tail. The fifth, his hand on the elephant's ear, said the animal was a huge fan. In the same way, the three hunters in this old Welsh song could not agree on anything. However, they had no excuse for their foolishness, since they could see very clearly.

Three Jolly Hunters

1. There were three jol-ly hunt-ers ___ a-hunt-ing one fine
2. They hunt-ed and they hal-loed ___ and noth-ing could they
3. They hunt-ed and they hal-loed ___ and noth-ing could they
4. They hunt-ed and they hal-loed ___ and noth-ing could they

day, And noth-ing could they find but ___ a light-house on the way. Look ye
find, But a horse a-run-ning through the woods, ___ and that they left be-hind. Look ye
find, But the moon up in the heav-ens, ___ and that they left be-hind. Look ye
find, But a bull-frog in the mill-pond, ___ and that they left be-hind. Look ye

there! One said it was a light-house,_____ the sec-ond he said, "Nay." The
there! One said it was a horse, but _____ the sec-ond he said, "Nay." The
there! One said it was the moon, but _____ the sec-ond he said, "Nay." The
there! One said it was a bull-frog,_____ the sec-ond he said, "Nay." The

third said, "It's a stee-ple _____ with the church blown clear a-way." Look ye there! _____
third said, "It's a rein-deer _ with the horns shot clear a-way." Look ye there! _____
third said, "It's a Hol-land cheese with the one-half cut a-way." Look ye there! _____
third said, "It's a night-in-gale with the feath-ers shaved a-way." Look ye there! _____

D.C. al FINE

PAN-AMERICAN DAY

April 14

MANY PEOPLE believe that "Pan-American" refers only to the Latin-American countries. But the holiday is one on which we salute all of our American neighbors, the nations to the south, and the great republic to the north. Our common border with Canada is such a peaceful one that we sometimes forget that she is a country with her own laws and her own respected place in the community of nations.

IN MANY PARTS of Canada, the people sing old British songs as if they had just come to the New World. Since our own country has many of these songs as a part of its song bag, we could easily present some British-American ballads from Kentucky and use them to represent Canadian folk music as well. There are many songs, however, that are native to Canada, and this dance song is one of them. It was born on the eastern coast and grew up among the fishermen of Newfoundland.

I's the B'y

Li - za.
grav - el.
corn - er.
but - ter.

Swing your part - ner, Sal - ly Tib-ble; Swing your part - ner, Sal - ly Brown.

mp

Swing your part - ner, ev - 'ry-one, All a-round the cir - cle.

1.

last time

[67]

&⸟ CANADA HAS TWO official languages, English and French. Her oldest songs are sung in a French language that, it is said, hasn't been spoken in France for three hundred years. The well-known song, "Alouette," may be as old as the oldest church built by the first French visitors to the New World. But the lark, the *Alouette*, is still one of their favorite birds, even though they sing, "*Je te plumerai la tête*," which means, "I will pluck your head."

Alouette

*your head †your nose ‡your eyes §your beak

plu - me- rai la tête, Et la tête, et la tête, A - lou- ette, A - lou- ette.
plu - me- rai le nez,
plu - me- rai les yeux,
plu - me- rai le bec,

Ah

Et le nez, et le nez, Et la tête, et la tête, A - lou -
Et les yeux, et les yeux, Et le nez, et le nez,
Et le bec, et le bec, Et les yeux, et les yeux,

ette, A - lou- ette. Ah

OTHER VERSES: 5. Et les ailes . . . [your wings]
6. Et la queue . . . [your tail]
7. Et le cou . . . [your neck]
8. Et les pattes . . . [your claws]

[69]

OUR SONG FOR French-Canada was dedicated to a lark. Our third Pan-American song is a Mexican melody about a little owl. The chorus is an imitation of the cry of the owl, so it may be appropriate for the singer to be owlish, as he sings "Poor little owl, you're so weary of flying."

Tecolote

Te- co-
Lit- tle

lo- te de Gua - da - ña,   pá - ja - ro ma-dru- ga - dor,   Te- co-
owl- et of Mex - i - co,   Sing- ing to me from a - bove.   Lit- tle

lo - te de Gua - da - ña,   Pá - ja - ro ma - dru - ga - dor,   Pres - tar -
owl - et of Mex - i - co,   Sing - ing to me from a - bove.   If your

ás   me tus a - li - tas,____ Pres - tar - ás   me tus a - li - tas,____ Presta -
wings   I could just bor - row,____ If your wings   I could just bor - row,____ If your

rás   me tus a - li - tas,____   Pa - ra ir ver a mi a - mor._____
wings   I could just bor - row,____   Then would I fly to my love._____

Chorus

rit.
__ Cu - cu - ri,   cu - ri, cu - ri cu,   Cu - cu - ri,   cu - ri, cu - ri
__ Cu - cu - ri,   cu - ri, cu - ri cu,   Cu - cu - ri,   cu - ri, cu - ri

rit.   a tempo

[71]

cu,   Cu - cu - ri,   cu - ri, cu - ri cu,_____   Po - bre - ci _____   to   te - co -
cu,   Cu - cu - ri,   cu - ri, cu - ri cu,_____   Lit - tle   owl _____   of ___   the

lo - te,_____   Ya   se   can - _____   sa   de   vo - _____ lar.
morn - ing,_____   Won't   you   please _____   lend   me   your   wings.

EASTER AND PASSOVER

ON THE SUNDAY following the first full moon after March 21st, the resurrection of Christ is celebrated. In England it was believed that the sun danced in the sky on Easter morning. Some people still wake up early on that day to see for themselves if the story is true.

The Hebrew celebration of Passover, which comes about the same time as Easter, brings with it other lovely stories—such as the Old Testament miracle of the parting of the waters of the Red Sea.

✒ AMERICA IS very fortunate in having acquired a large part of its population from Africa. The rhythms and syncopations of "The Dark Continent" influenced our music a great deal. Some of our finest religious songs can be found among the spirituals, which are the direct result of the meeting of the African chant and the western hymn. Our first Easter song is one of these.

That Great Getting-Up Morning

♩=80 (Lively)

1. Come and let me tell you 'bout the
ear - ly on a Fri - day when they
ear - ly on a Sun - day when he

ris - ing of the Sav - i - our, Fare thee well, fare thee well. Come and let me
laid him out to bur - y him, Fare thee well, fare thee well. Ear - ly on a
rose a - gain to glor - y, Fare thee well, fare thee well. Ear - ly on a

tell you 'bout the ris - ing of the Sav - i - our, Fare thee well, fare thee well.
Fri - day when they laid him out to bur - y him, Fare thee well, fare thee well.
Sun - day when he rose a - gain to glor - y, Fare thee well, fare thee well.

Chorus

On that great ___ get - ting up morn - ing Fare thee well, fare ___ thee well.

On that great get - ting - up morn - ing Fare thee well, fare ___ thee well. 2. It was well.
3. It was

time

[75]

THE EASTER HOLIDAY comes at the same time as the Hebrew celebration of Passover. It is believed that the old rhyme, "The House That Jack Built," comes from the Passover service. It is also believed that the song "Green Grow The Rushes" is a paraphrase of that part of the Passover service which begins, "Who knoweth thirteen? 'I,' saith Israel, 'knoweth thirteen.' " The chant continues, listing thirteen things, the last of which is, "One is God alone, Which is over Heaven and Earth."

Green Grow the Rushes–o

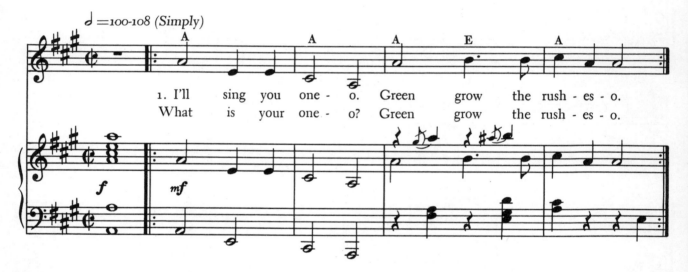

1. I'll sing you one - o. Green grow the rush - es - o.
What is your one - o? Green grow the rush - es - o.

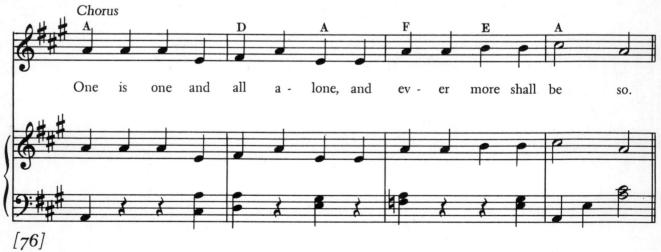

Chorus

One is one and all a - lone, and ev - er more shall be   so.

2. I'll sing you two - o. Green grow the rush - es - o.
What is your two - o? Green grow the rush - es - o.

Two is Paul and Si - las, And one is one and all a - lone, and

ev - er more shall be so. 3. I'll sing you three - o.
What is your three - o?

Green grow the rush - es - o.
Green grow the rush - es - o.

Three is the three from the far coun - try, And

two is Paul and Si - las, And one is one and all a - lone, and

ev - er more shall be so. 4. I'll sing you four - o.
What is your four - o?

Green grow the rush - es - o.
Green grow the rush - es - o. Four is the gos - pel preach - ers, And

three is the three from the far coun - try, And two is Paul and Si - las, And

[78]

one is one and all a - lone, and ev - er more shall be so.

5. I'll sing you five - o. Green grow the rush - es - o.
What is your five - o? Green grow the rush - es - o.

Five is the five who stayed a - live, And four is the gos - pel preach - ers, And

three is the three from the far coun - try, And two is Paul and Si - las, And

one is one and all a - lone, and ev - er more shall be so.

6. -(12.)* I'll sing you six - o. Green grow the rush - es - o.
sev - en - o. (etc.)

*For verses 7 through 12, sing successively the next higher number: seven, eight, nine, ten, eleven, twelve.

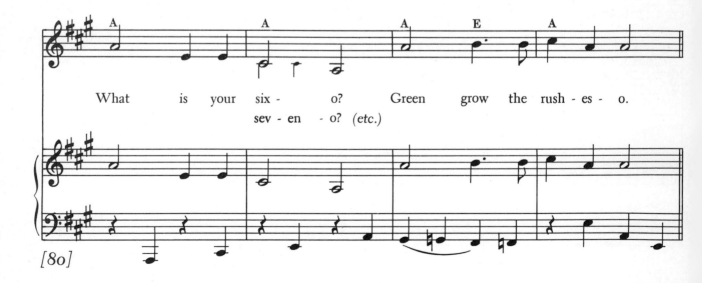

What is your six - o? Green grow the rush - es - o.
sev - en - o? (etc.)

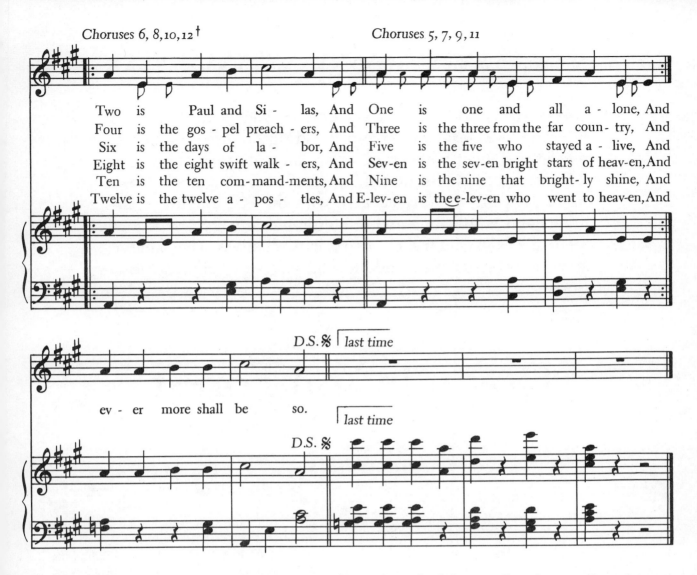

Choruses 6, 8, 10, 12 †   Choruses 5, 7, 9, 11

Two   is   Paul and Si - las, And One   is   one   and   all a - lone, And
Four is   the gos - pel preach - ers, And Three is the three from the far coun - try, And
Six   is   the days   of   la - bor, And Five   is the five who   stayed a - live, And
Eight is   the eight swift walk - ers, And Sev-en is the sev-en bright stars of heav-en, And
Ten   is   the ten com-mand-ments, And Nine is the nine that bright-ly shine, And
Twelve is the twelve a - pos - tles, And E-lev-en is the e-lev-en who went to heav-en, And

D.S. 𝄋 last time

ev - er   more shall be   so.   last time

D.S. 𝄋

†Each verse is followed by its chorus, which is then followed by each of the preceding choruses. Example: verse 4, chorus 4, 3, 2, 1; verse 5, chorus 5, 4, 3, 2, 1.

SOMETIMES A SONG doesn't say exactly what it means. Then, interpreters have a fine time discovering hundreds of hidden revelations about which they weave intricate relationships. In the year 1500, a collection of "ancient" songs included "Down in Yon Forest." It traveled here with the first English immigrants and is still sung and reinterpreted in widely separated sections of the country. On two points all agree. The "knight" is certainly Jesus Christ, and the song makes a wonderful Easter carol.

Down in Yon Forest

1. Down in yon for-est stands a — hall, Sing —
   in that hall there stands a — bed, Sing —
   on that bed there rests a — knight, Sing —
   by that bed there stands a — stone, Sing —

May, sing May, sing Mar - y. 'Tis cov-ered all o - ver with
May, sing May, sing Mar - y. 'Tis cov-ered all o - ver with
May, sing May, sing Mar - y. His wounds run blood by
May, sing May, sing Mar - y. With "Cor - pus Chris - ti"

purple and with pall, Sing all good men for the new-born babe. 2. And
scarlet and red, Sing all good men for the new-born babe. 3. And
day and night, Sing all good men for the new-born babe. 4. And
there-up-on, Sing all good men for the

B
last time e min.

new born-babe.

THE JEWISH HOLIDAY of Passover or *Pesach* is celebrated about the same time as the Easter holiday. It commemorates the sparing of the first-born of the Hebrew children and the escape from Egypt. The observance of Passover is today just as it was when Jesus and His disciples sat down around the *seder* table. This is a traditional song of thanksgiving, chanted at the Passover table.

Dayenu

Da - da - ye - nu,____ Da - da - ye - nu,____ Da - da - ye - nu, da -

ye - nu, da - ye - nu.____ ye - nu, da - ye - nu.

D. S. ⊕

[Even if you only delivered us from Egypt,
Even if you only gave us the Sabbath,
Even if you only gave us the Torah,
It is enough for us.]

[85]

ARBOR DAY

IN SOME STATES the Governor proclaims that one certain week shall be "Be Kind To Shoemakers Week," or that one day will be "National Nut Meat Day," and so on. But most states celebrate Arbor Day at the same time, although the Governor proclaims it as a special occasion each year. On this day we are asked to remember that our forests are important to our daily lives, and are not indestructible. Care and caution will mean more paper, magazines, houses, and better land conservation for the nation.

EVERYONE HAS a special tree somewhere in his memory. Even city dwellers can recall with fondness some crooked little tree halfway up the block, or somewhere in the park. Some people will think, with a smile, of the Christmas tree and its gay trimmings. Others will remember a tree that was shading them when some pleasant incident occurred.

The Juniper Tree

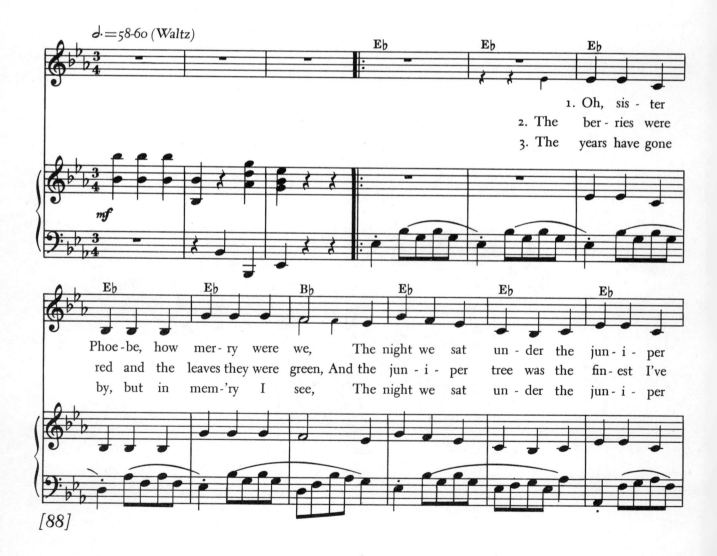

1. Oh, sis - ter
2. The ber - ries were
3. The years have gone

Phoe - be, how mer - ry were we, The night we sat un - der the jun - i - per
red and the leaves they were green, And the jun - i - per tree was the fin - est I've
by, but in mem'ry I see, The night we sat un - der the jun - i - per

tree.
seen. The jun - i - per tree, hi - o, hi - o, The jun - i - per
tree.

tree, hi - o. o.

[89]

LIKE the "Yonders Tree," "The Tree in the Wood" is a cumulative song. That means that the singer keeps piling verses one on top of another until the song gets top-heavy and he forgets the verses he's just sung. In the earliest version of this song, which is still heard in England, the singer adds verses until he's back where he started—and very happy to be there, too.

The Tree in the Wood

1. All in the wood there was a tree, The pret-ti-est tree that you

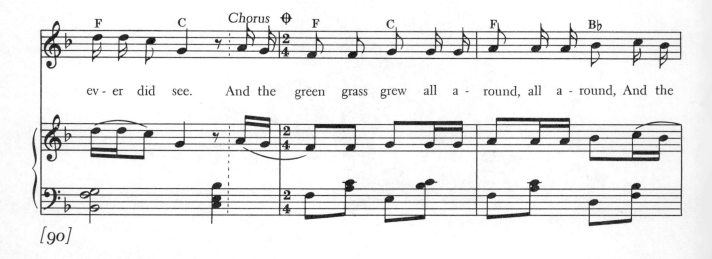

ev-er did see. And the green grass grew all a-round, all a-round, And the

green grass grew all a - round.   2. And

on that tree there was a branch, The pret - ti - est branch that you

ev - er did see. Branch on the tree, And the tree in the wood. And the green grass grew all a -

round, all a - round, And the green grass grew all a - round.   3. And

on that branch there was a nest, The pret- ti - est nest that you

ev - er did see. Nest on the branch, And the branch on the tree, And the tree in the

Chorus

wood. And the green grass grew all a - round, all a-round, And the green grass grew all a -

round. 4. And in that nest there was an egg, The

pret-ti- est egg   that you ev- er did   see.   Egg in the   nest, And the nest   on   the

branch, And the branch on the   tree,   And the tree   in the wood.   And the

green grass grew all a- round, all a-round, And the green grass grew   all a - round.

5. And   on that egg,   there sat a bird,   The pret-ti- est bird   that you

ev- er did see. Bird on the egg, And the egg in the nest, And the nest on the

branch, And the branch on the tree, And the tree in the wood.

Chorus

And the

green grass grew all a- round, all a-round, And the green grass grew all a - round.

6. And on that bird,   there was a feath-er,   The pret-ti-est feath-er   that you
7. And from that feather   they made a bed,   The pret-ti-est bed   that you
8. And on that bed   there lay a maid,   The pret-ti-est maid   that you
9. And from that maid   there was a child,   The pret-ti-est child   that you
10. And then the child,   it plant-ed a seed,   The pret-ti-est seed   that you
11. And from that seed   there grew a tree,   The pret-ti-est tree   that you

THE TREE in this song is a "feeding" tree—that is, all the farm-feeding seems to take place next to it. There is no mention in the many versions of this song of any other arboreal function. It might also have been a shade tree, or a fruit tree, or a hammock-hanging tree, but the song doesn't mention any of these. It is generally agreed among reliable authorities, however, that a yonders tree is a tree which can be found "somewhere out there."

Yonders Tree

1. I love my roost-er, my roost-er loves me; I feed my roost-er by yon - ders tree.

My lit-tle roost-er goes cock-a-doo-doo, Doo dood-le, doo dood-le, doo doo._____

Verse 2

2. I love my cat and my cat loves me; I feed my cat un-der yon-ders tree.

My lit-tle cat__ goes meow, meow, meow, My lit-tle roost-er goes cock-a-doo-doo, Doo

Chorus

Verse 3

dood-le, doo dood-le, doo doo._____ 3. I love my crow and my crow loves me;

ha, ha, ha, my lit-tle crow__ goes caw, caw, caw, My lit-tle

Chorus

cat__ goes meow, meow, meow, My lit-tle roost-er goes cock - a- doo-doo, Doo

Verse 5

dood-le, doo dood-le, doo doo._____ 5. I love my g'raffe and my g'raffe loves me;

I feed my g'raffe un - der yon - ders tree. My lit - tle g'raffe__ goes

My lit-tle hy - e - na goes ha, ha, ha, My lit-tle crow__ goes caw, caw, caw, My lit-tle cat__ goes meow, meow, meow,

Chorus

My lit-tle roost-er goes cock - a-doo-doo, Doo dood-le, doo dood-le, doo doo._____

MAY DAY

May 1

⟨⟨ For centuries May Day was one of the really important events of the year. Everyone danced around the Maypole, sang May carols, and, in general, gave the month a grand welcome. The cutting of Mayflowers, the marriage of a May bride to a May groom, the carrying of garlands to each household is no longer a part of our yearly life, but some of the superstitions and many of the songs still persist.

IT IS CUSTOMARY to select one special flower as the Mayflower. In America we usually choose the lovely arbutus which blooms with special beauty in May. In some sections of the country other plants are favored, but whichever blossom is chosen, it is referred to for the day as the "mayflower", or as the "may". Our carol is English in origin and is still sung with great vigor in the southern Appalachian Mountains. If you wish to sing it, you, too, must sing it with great vigor.

The May Carol

♩=80 (Simply)

1. This morn - ing _ is the month _ of _ May, The fin - est of the _
brought _ you _ here a bunch _ of _ may, Be - fore your door it _
wan - dered _ far, through all _ the _ night, And al - so through the _
song _ is _ done, I will be _ gone, I can no long - er _

year. Good _ peo - ple _ all, both great _ and small, I
stands. It's _ well set _ out, and well _ spread out, And
day. And _ when I _ come your way _ a - gain, I'll
stay. God _ bless you _ all, both great _ and small, And

wish you__ joy - ful cheer._____ 2. I've
fash - ioned__ by God's hand._____ 3. I've
bring a__ branch of may._____ 4. My
send a__ joy - ful May._____

IN THE SOUTH, there are still countless superstitions connected with May Day. They say that if one looks down a well on that day, one will see one's future wife. Some believe that the May-flower will cure many ills if rubbed on the afflicted parts. In Louisiana, we were assured that washing one's face with May morning dew would guarantee a clear complexion all the year around. The following song, however, is not the result of some superstitious belief. It probably uses the "May Day in the Morning" chorus only because it sings easily.

'Twas May Day in the Morning

♩ =80 (Deliberately)

1. There was a crow sat on a stone, He
was a cat skinned up a tree, To
was a roost-er in a trough, Who
was a farm-er made a wish, That

flew a-way and there was none. An-oth-er came and there was one, 'Twas
see what-ev-er was to see. When he fell down then down fell he, 'Twas
got a touch of whoop-ing cough. He sneezed his tail and feath-ers off, 'Twas
he could swim like an-y fish. They popped him in the chaf-ing dish, 'Twas

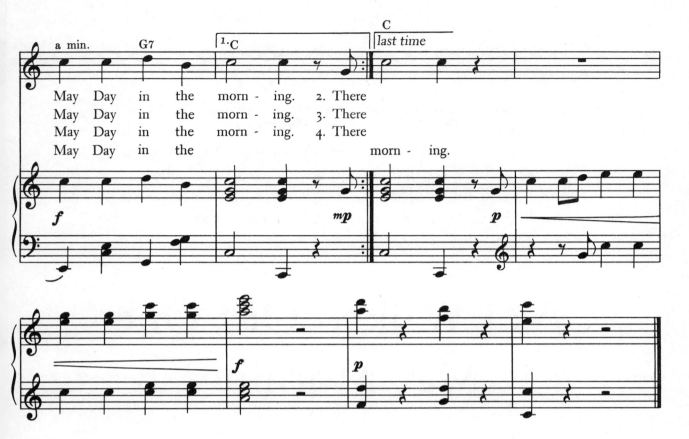

May Day in the morn - ing. 2. There
May Day in the morn - ing. 3. There
May Day in the morn - ing. 4. There
May Day in the morn - ing.

5. There was a man who grew so fat,
   He always stuck in his rocking chair.
   It doesn't rhyme but I don't care—
   'Twas May Day in the morning.

MAY MORNING is mentioned in many old love songs. Even the sad song about Barbara Allen and her lost love begins on a May morning. It's difficult to select any one of the May-morn love songs because that means not using all the others. Our choice has a lively lilt to it, is of a respectable age—possibly three hundred years old—and is still popular where folk songs are a part of the daily existence.

As I Walked Out One May Morning

1. As I walked out one May morn-ing Just
   old are you, my pret-ty lit-tle miss, How
   cheeks were tipped a cher-ry red, Her
   went down to her moth-er's house The

as the sun was ris-ing, I ov-er-took a fine young maid; She
old are you, my hon-ey? She an-swered me with a "Tee hee hee," I'm
hair hung down her shoul-der, She had a dark and a rol-ling eye, And a
moon was shin-ing clear-ly. Oh, mar-ry me, my pret-ty lit-tle miss, For

Chorus

looked at me sur - pris - ing.
"Sev - en - teen next Sun - day."   I'm go - ing to the meet - ing, do you
smile that grew much bold - er.
I do love you dear -   ly.

want to come a - long?   I'm   go - ing to the meet - ing, do you

want to come a - long?   I'm   go - ing to the meet - ing, do you

want to come a - long? We'll dance by the light of the moon.　2. How moon.

3. Her

4. I

5. I can't come down, I won't come down,
   No use for you to tarry.
   But come next May and ask again,
   I'm over young to marry.

MOTHER'S DAY

Second Sunday in May

FOR A LONG TIME America had no Mother's Day. When a Mother's Day celebration was first suggested, cynical people protested that it was just an attempt by florists and candy-makers to sell their wares. It may be true that florists and candy-makers were among the first to support a special day for mothers, but the rest of the nation wasn't far behind. We all know that mothers deserve, if not a whole year, at least a day of appreciation.

IT IS GENERALLY agreed that mothers and children go together. And it is further accepted that one of the best known results of this collaboration is the lullaby. According to a very reliable authority, the majority of lullabies say, in one form or another, "Go to sleep, all is well and mother is here." Our first song for Mother's Day, however, is really an old-fashioned list of the work a mother must do if she's to be an all-around mother. The word "greet" in the song shows its Scottish origin, because in old Scotland "to greet" meant "to cry."

Can Ye Sew Cushions

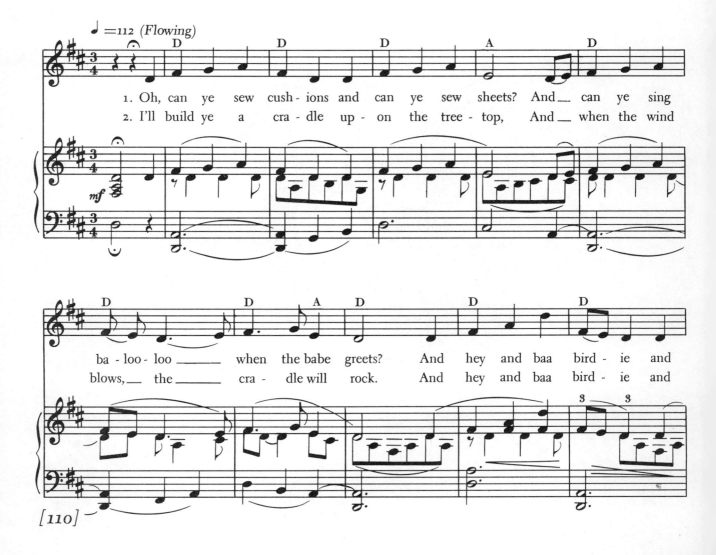

1. Oh, can ye sew cush-ions and can ye sew sheets? And can ye sing ba-loo-loo when the babe greets? And hey and baa bird-ie and

2. I'll build ye a cra-dle up-on the tree-top, And when the wind blows, the cra-dle will rock. And hey and baa bird-ie and

hey and baa lamb, And hey and baa bird - ie, my wee bon - nie lamb.
hey lil - ly loo, And hey and baa bird - ie, my wee bon - nie lamb.

Chorus: Hee - o, wee - o, what can___ I do wi' you? But I can - na do with -

out you. Mon - ey - o I have lit - tle to give you,

But I can - na do with - out you.

As time goes by and the child becomes an adult, the normal mother often develops a remarkable visual aberration. She looks at a grown man or woman and sees a tiny baby. This can be very annoying to the grownup who doesn't like to be thought of as a child. Occasionally, however, it's a comfort to have some person who sees you as innocent and lovable despite your faults. This American-made cowboy song shows that even the baddest of the bad-men appreciated their mothers.

When the Work's All Done

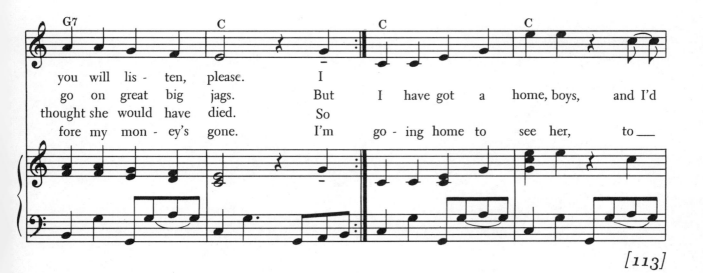

you will lis - ten, please.   I
go on great big jags.   But   I have got a home, boys,   and I'd
thought she would have died.   So
fore my mon - ey's gone.   I'm   go - ing home to   see her,   to ___

like to   see   it   all,   So I'm going to   see   my   moth- er   when the
heed my moth - er's call;   I'm _ go - ing home to   moth- er   when the

work's all done this   fall."
work's all done this   fall."

2. "When

2.

"MAN'S WORK LASTS from sun to sun; woman's work is never done." It is remarkable that mothers have time for their countless chores *and* raising their children, too. Today, there are many laborsaving devices in the home, but the work still stretches ahead of the woman-of-the-house like an endless road. An old song from Scotland, now at home in our country, tells how the farmer learned to recognize this fact.

Old Grumbler

♩ =100 (Lively)

1. Old Grum-bler swore by the shirt he wore And the green leaves up on the tree, That he could do more work in a day, Than his
2. Well, she turned on her heel and went to the field And left him the lad-le-o. He was stir-ring the pot and he soon for - got, He should
3. Then he went to watch the speck-led hen For fear she'd go a - stray, And he dropped the yarn in the mid-dle of the barn, And
4. Then he looked to the east and he looked to the west And he saw the set-ting sun, And he saw his wife on her way back home, And his

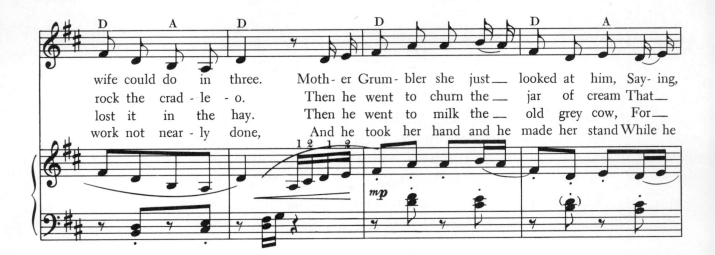

wife could do in three. Moth-er Grum-bler she just ___ looked at him, Say-ing,
rock the crad - le - o. Then he went to churn the ___ jar of cream That ___
lost it in the hay. Then he went to milk the ___ old grey cow, For ___
work not near-ly done, And he took her hand and he made her stand While he

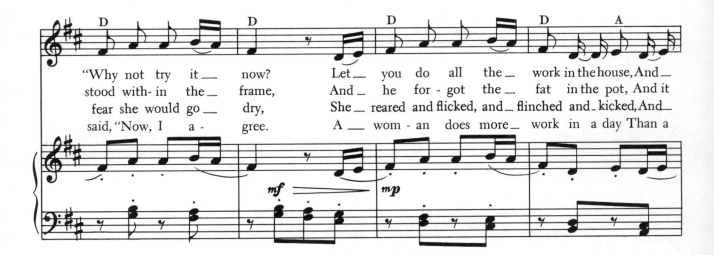

"Why not try it ___ now? Let ___ you do all the ___ work in the house, And ___
stood with-in the ___ frame, And ___ he for-got the ___ fat in the pot, And it
fear she would go ___ dry, She ___ reared and flicked, and ___ flinched and ___ kicked, And
said, "Now, I a - gree. A ___ wom-an does more ___ work in a day Than a

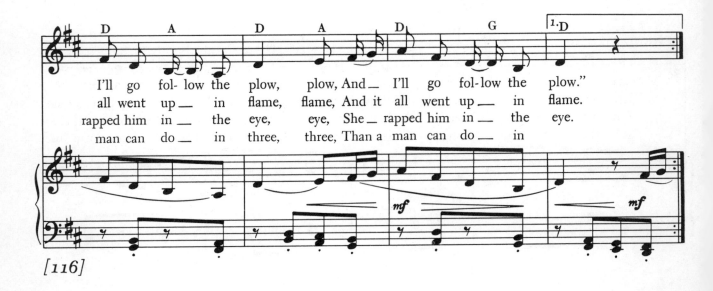

I'll go fol-low the plow, plow, And ___ I'll go fol-low the plow."
all went up ___ in flame, flame, And it all went up ___ in flame.
rapped him in ___ the eye, eye, She ___ rapped him in ___ the eye.
man can do ___ in three, three, Than a man can do ___ in

ARMED FORCES DAY

By Presidential Proclamation

⁓§ EVERY YEAR on Army Day there used to be a parade of America's armed might on the streets of our towns and cities. The Navy, too, had a day for parading. The Navy couldn't march its battleships down Broadway, but it could show off its sailors, marines, and small arms. The Air Force had no day but felt it deserved recognition, too. And so all the services are honored on one day, "Armed Forces Day," and everyone parades at once.

One of our first real soldier songs was written by General Joseph Warren in June, 1775. Warren was the Minute Man who started Paul Revere off on his ride through every Middlesex village and town. In writing his defiant words, the General adopted one of Britain's best marching songs. In the same month of June, while commanding his troops at the battle of Bunker Hill, General Warren was shot down. But his song has never died, and is included here as our Armed Forces Song.

Free Amerikay

♩=100 (Vigorously)

1. Torn from a world of ty- rants, Be- neath this west- ern sky,
up your hands, ye he- roes, And swear with proud dis-
bless this maid- en clim- ate, And through its vast do-
fu- ture day shall crown us The mas- ters of the

sky, We formed a new do- min- ion, A land of lib- er- tie. The
dain, The wretch that would en- snare you Shall lay his snares in vain. Should
main, May hosts of he- roes clus- ter Who scorn to wear a chain. Then
main; Our fleets shall speak in thun- der To Eng- land, France, and Spain. And

world shall own we're mas - ters here, Then has - ten on __ the __ day __ Huz -
Eu - rope emp - ty all her force, We'll meet her in __ ar - ray, __ And
guard your rights, A - mer - i - cans, Nor stoop to law - less __ sway, __ Op -
na - tions o'er the o - cean spread Shall trem - ble and __ o - bey, __ The

za, huz - za, huz - za, huz - za for __ free A - mer - i - kay. 2. Lift
fight and __ shout, and __ fight and __ shout, for __ North A - mer - i - kay. 3. God
pose, op - pose, op - pose, op - pose for __ North A - mer - i - kay. 4. Some
sons, the __ sons, the __ sons, the __ sons of __ free A - mer - i -

non legato

Last time

kay.

ONCE WHEN I was presenting a program of folk songs, I was requested to sing the song of the Norwich knights. I didn't know any such song, and went on to sing, instead, "Old King Cole," which I had learned as a marching song in the American Army. I was then told that "Old King Cole" was once the song of the Norwich knights, and that it had been sung in England in the days when London Bridge was just a plank, and *Beowulf* was the Book-of-the-Month.

Old King Cole

♩=112 (Vigorously)

1. Old King Cole was a merry old soul and a merry old soul was he; He called for his pipe, and he called for his bowl, and he called for his pri - vates* three.

2. Old King Cole was a merry old soul and a merry old soul was he; He called for his pipe, and he called for his bowl, and he called ___ for his corp' - rals* three.

Substitute the next highest rank for each succeeding verse.

Chorus
(*repeat as necessary*)

1. "Cheer, cheer, cheer," said the pri - vates, "Mer - ry men are we. There are
2. "Hut two, hut two, hut," said the corp' - rals.("*Cheer, cheer, etc.*)

none so fair as can com - pare with the fight - ing in - fant -

D.S. ⊕ | last time

ry."

D.S. ⊕

OTHER VERSES: 3. "Right by squads, squads right," said the sergeants...
4. "We do all the work," said the shavetails . . .
5. "We want a ten-day leave," said the captains . . .
6. "What's my next command?" said the majors . . .
7. "Shine my boots and spurs," said the colonels . . .
8. "Cheer, cheer, cheer," said the generals . . .

When the generals say, "Cheer," everyone else, down to the
privates, sings "Cheer."

THE MARINES have fought in every American war since the French and Indian War, and they're a very proud branch of the Armed Services. But they always seem annoyed when reminded that they have to be transported by the Navy. When John Paul of Scotland became an American Captain, he carried a full complement of Marines aboard his ship. And he named the vessel *The Bonhomme Richard* for the *Poor Richard's Almanac* of Benjamin Franklin. With his fighting crew, Captain Jones won some of the most exciting battles of naval history.

An American Frigate

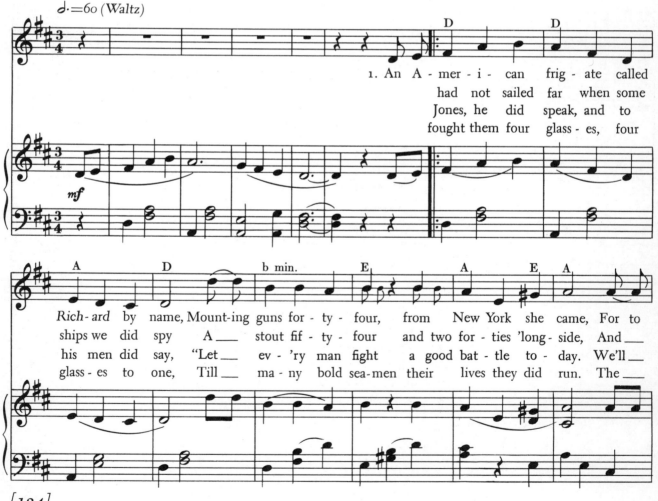

1. An A - mer - i - can frig - ate called
had not sailed far when some
Jones, he did speak, and to
fought them four glass - es, four

Rich - ard by name, Mount - ing guns for - ty - four, from New York she came, For to
ships we did spy A ___ stout fif - ty - four and two for - ties 'long - side, And ___
his men did say, "Let ___ ev - 'ry man fight a good bat - tle to - day. We'll ___
glass - es to one, Till ___ ma - ny bold sea - men their lives they did run. The ___

cruise in the chan-nel of old Eng-land's fame, With a no-ble com-mand-er, Paul
twen-ty bold ship-pen all lad-en with store, And the con-voy was in for the
take that bold con-voy in the height of her pride, Or the *Rich-ard* shall found-er and
shot flew so hot, boys, we could n't stand it long, When the brave Brit-ish col-ors came

Jones was his name.
old York-shire shore.
sink in the tide."
fin-al-ly down.

2. We —
3. Paul —
4. We —

THE AIR FORCE is our youngest service branch. Most of its songs are parodies of tunes already veterans of countless campaigns. Some popular songs have been written which might do very well as theme songs, but we've decided to volunteer the following as our contribution to the song bag of the Air Force.

The Air Force

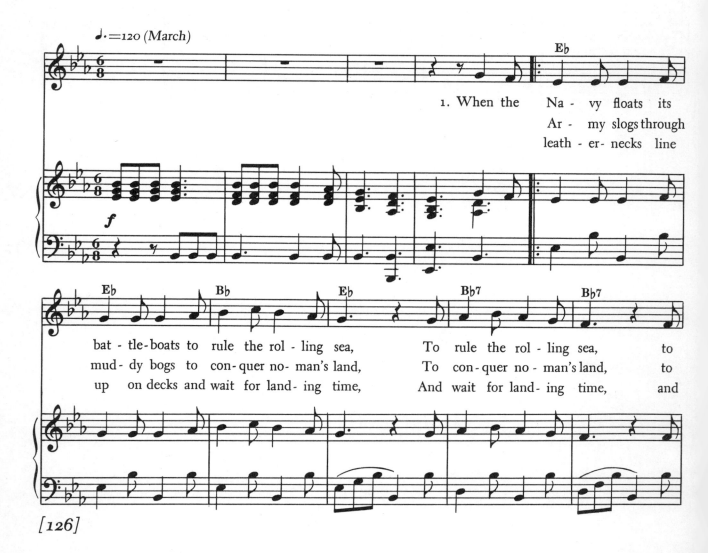

1. When the Na - vy floats its
   Ar - my slogs through
   leath - er - necks line

bat - tle-boats to rule the rol - ling sea,   To rule the rol - ling sea,   to
mud - dy bogs to con - quer no - man's land,   To con - quer no - man's land,   to
up on decks and wait for land - ing time,   And wait for land - ing time,   and

rule the rol - ling sea,
con - quer no - man's land,
wait for land - ing time,

They hear a roar, ten G's or more, and look up in the
They hear a sound, they turn a-round, and see in proud ar -
They search the skies with start-led eyes as bombs be-gin to

Chorus

sky, As the Air Force flies right by.
ray,___ The Air Force on its way.
burst;___ The Air Force got there first.

The

Air Force, the Air Force, that's the force for me. The Air Force, the

Air   Force,   that's the force for me.

1.   Bb   last time

2. When the
3. When the

MEMORIAL DAY

May 30

THERE ARE MORE SONGS from the War Between the States than from any other conflict in which this country participated. Every day while the fighting raged, new songs were being published, printed in the newspapers, distributed without cost to the soldiers, or rewritten under fire. On May 30th we honor the brave men who faced each other under two differing American flags, and we are almost embarrassed when we try to choose a few from among the wonderful songs of the time.

AT FIRST, the soldier songs of the War Between the States were brave, spirited songs about ideals and principles. But, as the war continued, many soldiers began to make up ditties complaining about their hard lot. One of these was written by a southern soldier, probably while he was standing guard at some battle-worn outpost. The song is especially noteworthy because the author signed his name to it, which is very unusual in folk music.

The Soldier's Life

1. How lit-tle you good peo-ple know What we poor sol-diers un-der-go, When
times we lie on the cold, cold ground, Where there's no shel-ter to be found; Some-
break of day the Yan-kees come, They play the fife and beat the drum, Dis-
as to food, there's not e-nough, The bread is stale, the beef is tough; But,

called up - on to __ take up arms And rid our
times it rains, some - times it snows. The howl - ing
turb the sol - dier's sweet re - pose; He ris - es
still and all, we __ don't com - plain Some day we'll

g min.

coun - try __ of a - larms. 2. Some -
wind a - bout us blows. 3. At
and puts __ on his clothes. 4. And
get good __ food a - gain.

5. You want to know who wrote this song?
   I'll tell you now, it won't take long.
   It was composed by A. B. Wright,
   Who walked his post one rainy night.

[131]

As the War continued, the soldiers of the South found themselves fighting in ragged uniforms with very meager rations. The Union blockade prevented supplies from reaching the South by way of its seaports, and Grant's capture of Vicksburg brought the Mississippi River under Union control. The southern infantryman was forced to rely on peanuts as a major source of energy. After a while, he looked upon these "goober peas" with great distaste and he sang about them with bitter satire.

Goober Peas

♩=126 (March, Lightly half serious)

1. Sit - ting by the road - side, on a sum - mer day,
2. When a horse - man pass - es, the sol - diers have a rule, To
3. Just be - fore the bat - tle, the Gen - 'ral hears a row; He

think my song has last - ed just a - bout e - nough. The

Chat - ting with my mess - mates, to pass the time a - way,
cry out at their loud - est, "Farm - er, where's your mule?"
says, "The Yanks are com - ing, I hear their rif - les now."

Ly - ing in the
But an - oth - er
He looks on down the

sub - ject's in - ter - est - ing, but the rhymes are might - y rough. I wish the war was

shad - ow,   un - der - neath the   trees,   Good - ness, how de - li - cious,
cus - tom, en - chant - ing - er   than   these   Is   wear - ing out your grind - ers
road - way and what d'you think he   sees?   The Geor -   gia   Mi - li - tia
o - ver   so   free   from rags and fleas,   We'd kiss   our wives and sweet - hearts, say good-

eat - ing goo - ber   peas.
eat - ing goo - ber   peas.   Peas, peas, peas, peas, eat - ing goo - ber peas Good - ness, how de -
crack - ing goo - ber   peas.
bye to goo - ber   peas.

li - cious,   eat - ing goo - ber   peas.

4. I

HENRY C. WORK of Connecticut wrote many popular songs of the day. His "Grandfather's Clock" is still well-known. But the soldiers of the northern armies loved his "Nicodemus Awake," "Babylon Is Falling," "Grafted Into the Army," "Marching Through Georgia," and "Kingdom Coming." The last is still sung, as "Jubilo," and it's popular even in the South, although it was written to show how happy the slaves were when they were freed by the Union Army.

Jubilo

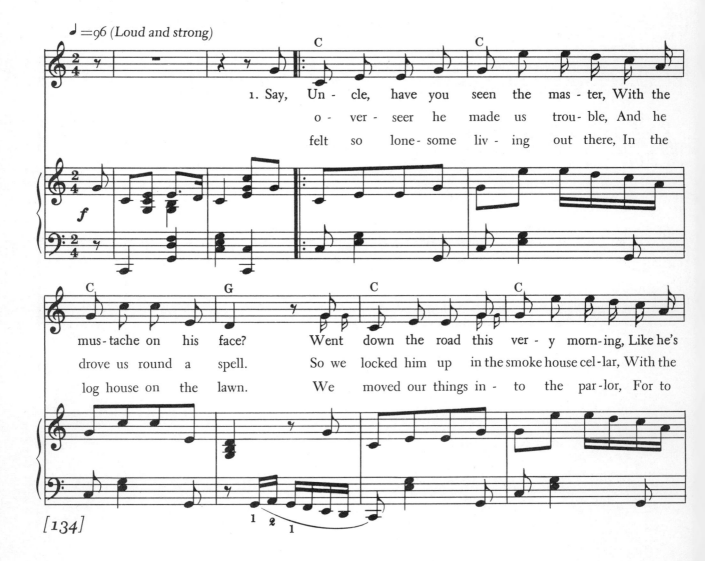

going to leave the place. He saw the smoke from down the riv- er, Where the
key thrown down the well. The whip is lost, the hand- cuff bro-ken, And the
keep it while he's gone. There's bread and cheese all in the kitch-en, And I

Lin - coln gun - boats lay; He grabbed his hat and left ver-y sud- den, And I
mas-ter'll have his pay. He's old e-nough, big e-nough, ought to've known bet-ter Than to
guess we'll all have some. I sup-pose they'll all be con - fis - ca-ted When the

think he's run - a - way.
try and run a - way. **Chorus** The mas - ter run, hah, hah,
Lin-coln sol - diers come. The mas - ter run, hoh,

hoh. It must be now the King-dom com-ing, And the year of Ju - bi -

lo.

1.

last time

2. The
3. We

FATHER'S DAY

Third Sunday in June

◆§ FATHERS ARE prevented from spending more time with their children by the necessity of making enough money to support them. Therefore, one day is set aside each year on which each of us is reminded of his hard-working male parent. It isn't required that we buy him neckties which don't match his clothes, or tobacco which causes him to cough. All that is required on Father's Day is that we treat him gently and perhaps say one or two kind words to him.

THE IMMIGRANTS who came to America used up most of their savings to purchase their transportation. They performed back-breaking tasks to support their households and finance the daily life of the family. In turn, they expected a great deal from their children. In this song, to the tune of a well-known nursery song, the singer uses a "cumulative" refrain, possibly to emphasize the amount of work he had to do.

When I First Came to This Land

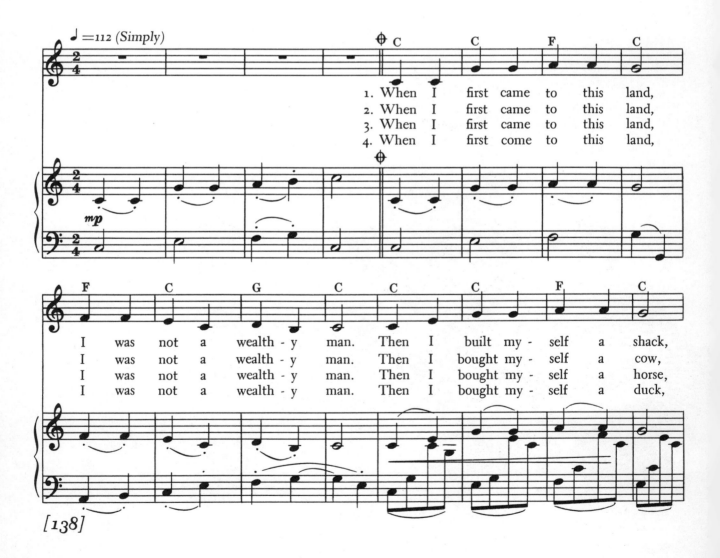

♩=112 (Simply)

1. When I first came to this land, I was not a wealth-y man. Then I built my-self a shack,
2. When I first came to this land, I was not a wealth-y man. Then I bought my-self a cow,
3. When I first came to this land, I was not a wealth-y man. Then I bought my-self a horse,
4. When I first come to this land, I was not a wealth-y man. Then I bought my-self a duck,

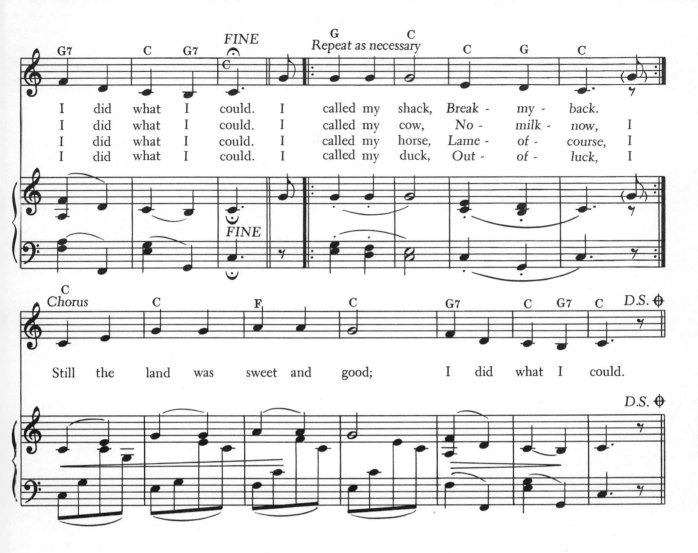

I did what I could. I called my shack, Break - my - back.
I did what I could. I called my cow, No - milk - now, I
I did what I could. I called my horse, Lame - of - course, I
I did what I could. I called my duck, Out - of - luck, I

Chorus

Still the land was sweet and good; I did what I could.

5. When I first came to this land,
   I was not a wealthy man.
   Then I got myself a wife—
   I did what I could.
   I called my wife, *Run-for-your-life*,
   I called my duck, *Out-of-luck*,
   I called my horse, *Lame-of-course*,
   I called my cow, *No-milk-now*,
   I called my shack, *Break-my-back*.
      CHORUS

6. When I first came to this land,
   I was not a wealthy man.
   Then I got myself a son—
   I did what I could.
   I told my son: "My work's done."
      CHORUS: For the land was sweet and good;
            I did what I could.

HERE'S A SONG which may have been composed fairly recently but has already traveled to Canada and the far north by way of the human voice. Even serious composers have been taken by the sprightly melody, and it's a part of "Billy The Kid," a ballet by Aaron Copland. The writer of the song points out in the last verse that he, too, is a father. And he doesn't understand how "Great-Granddad" managed so many children.

Great-Granddad

1. Great - Grand - dad, when the land was young, Barred the door with a
2. Great - Grand - dad was a bus - y man; Washed his face in a
3. Twen-ty - one chil - dren came to bless The lit - tle log hut in the
4. Twen-ty - one chil - dren and how they grew Big and strong on a

wag - on tongue; Al - ways kept his barn door locked,
fry - ing pan, Shaved his beard with a hunt - ing knife, And he
wil - der - ness. He ruled them all with an i - ron rod, And he
mut - ton stew. Twen-ty - three meals three times a day, No

Said his prayers with his rif-le cocked.
wore one suit for __ all his life.
filled them full of the fear of God.
won-der that Grand-ma's hair turned gray.

5. Twenty-one kids and how they grew
   Strong and tall like their father, too.
   Twenty-one kids, but his great-grandson—
   He has a terrible time with one.

EVERY ONCE IN AWHILE, the wise father will bring a present home for his child so that the child will appear happy to see him on future occasions. A carpenter may bring a toy he's made in the shop. A teacher may show the child a pretty drawing made by one of his students. A banker may bring home some shiny, new, thousand-dollar bills. The father in this song is probably a fisherman and, since the song is over a hundred years old, he is probably, by now, a very old fisherman.

Dance to Your Daddy

♩ =96 (Dance like)

1. Dance to your dad-dy, my lit-tle lad-die,
2. Dance to your dad-dy, my lit-tle lad-die,

Dance to your dad-dy, my____ lit-tle man. You may have a fish,
Dance to your dad-dy, my____ lit-tle man. When you are a man and

you may have a fin, You may have a had-dock, when the boat comes in.
fit to take a wife, You will wed a maid and love her all your life.

You will have a cod-ling boiled__ in a pan; Dance to your dad - dy,
She will be your las - sie, you will be her man; Dance to your dad - dy,

my__ lit - tle man.
my__ lit - tle man.

FLAG DAY

June 14

◦§ WHEN ONE PERFORMS the same act over and over again, it often becomes a dull, meaningless habit. Many people recite the pledge to the flag without thinking about the meaning of the words. In fact, few Americans can accurately draw a picture of the flag itself. Yet, that flag is a symbol of the principles for which this nation stands. And many of our folk songs are based on the inspiring events which surround the story of the flag.

One of the great marching songs of the War Between the States was "Marching Along." It was written for the North, but southern soldiers adopted it because it had a lively beat and an adaptable set of verses. Wherever it was sung, North or South, the name of the "leader" was changed each time a new general was chosen. The southerners used "Lee" throughout the war. The Union troops began with "McClellan" and finished with "Grant."

Marching Along

1. The flag of our coun-try is float-ing on high, We'll stand by that flag un-til we con-quer or die. Mc-

2. Our wives and chil-dren we leave far be-hind, Our work and our pleas-ure to bat-tle re-signed; The

3. The foe is be-fore us in bat-tle ar-ray, But let us not wav-er or turn from our way. Our

Clel- lan's our lead - er, he's gal-lant and strong; For God and for coun-try we'll go
flag is our stand-ard, the Lord is our song; With cour - age and faith,— we'll go
cause is a just one, the foe's in the wrong, For God and for coun-try, we'll go

march-ing a - long.
march-ing a - long.
march-ing a - long.

THERE ARE very few love songs which might be appropriate for Flag Day. In fact, I don't know of any, excepting this one. Originally, this was an English song, but it became very popular among the people who lived and worked on the American frontier. When the war began with Mexico, it was practically an anthem among the defenders of the Alamo. Some people say that the reason Mexicans called the Americans *Gringos* was that Americans always sang this song.

Green Grow the Lilacs

1. Green grow the li - lacs all cov - ered with dew. I'm
passed my love's win - dow both ear - ly and late, The
sent my love let - ters all scent - ed with rue, I
make for the bor - der and join in the fray, Till

lone - ly, my dar - ling, since part - ing from you. But by our next meet - ing, I
look that she gave me, it made my heart break. The look that she gave me, it
sent my love let - ters that said, "I love you." She sent back my let - ters all
Tex - as is free and we call it a day; And at our next meet - ing my

hope you'll prove true, When I trade the green li - lacs for the Red, White, and Blue. 2. I
made my heart rue, Mean - ing, "I love an - oth - er one___ bet - ter than you." 3. I
wrapped up in twine, Say - ing, "You go with your love and ___ I'll go with mine." 4. I'll
love will prove true, For I've changed the green li - lacs for the Red, White and Blue.

Last time D.C. al FINE 𝄋

A CERTAIN DR. BEANES made the error of taking prisoner three British soldiers during the War of 1812, although he was a civilian, and the British were in possession of the neighboring countryside. He was imprisoned aboard a British ship and a friend, Francis Scott Key, arranged for his release. While they were waiting to go ashore, the British bombarded Fort McHenry, near Baltimore, and Key wrote the song which became our national anthem. The melody used was once a British drinking song, and later was a eulogy for George Washington.

The Star-Spangled Banner

Should the tem - pest of war, o - ver-shad - ow our land, Its bolts could not
Oh, __ say, can you see, by the dawn's ear - ly light, What so proud - ly we

rend Free-dom's tem - ple a - sun - der. For un-moved at the por - tals would __
hailed at the twi - light's last gleam - ing? Whose broad stripes and bright stars, __ through the

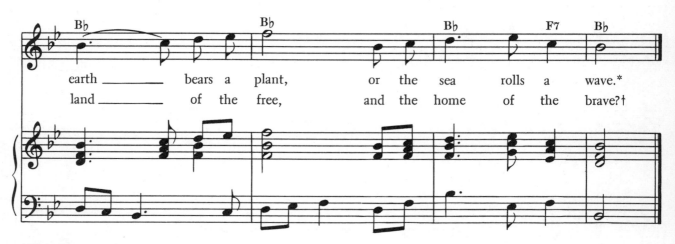

earth _____ bears a plant, or the sea rolls a wave.*

land _____ of the free, and the home of the brave?†

*This first verse is the Eulogy to General George Washington.

†This verse, of course, is the familiar first part of our national anthem.

SUMMER

SUMMER IS vacation time. The earth has made arrangements with the sun which guarantee warmer weather at this time in most of our states. Since summer months are vacation months, dance and game songs are to be found in great abundance. And since summer is a lazy, lounging time, there are many indolent summer melodies.

IN THE THIRTEENTH CENTURY a monk named John of Fornsete wrote down the words and music for a group song known as "Sumer Is Icumen In." Today we can sing the same words and, except for "verteth," understand what we are singing. We hereby reveal that "verteth" means "seeks the green meadow."

WHEN THIS SONG is sung as a canon, the piano should be omitted and the voices should enter as follows: bass I, bass II (see bottom of page 155), upper voices I to IV as indicated. The bass part should be repeated until the canon ends. The fermata (⌢) indicates possible endings when sung as a canon, or the work may end by allowing the voices to drop out as each finishes its part. The two bass parts, however, always end together.

Summer Is A-Coming In

♩. = 100 (Lightly)

I
Sum - mer is a - com - ing in____

II
Loud - ly sing, cuck- oo.

III
Grow - eth seed and blow- eth mead, And springs the wood a-

new   Sing,   cuck - oo.   Ewe now bleat-eth af - ter lamb, Low'th af - ter calf the

cow,   Bul- lock start-eth, buck now vert-eth Mer - ry sing, cuck-oo.   Cuck - oo,

cuck - oo —— Well sing'st thou, cuck-oo —— Nor cease thou nev- er   now.

To be sung only when performed as a canon.

bass I

Sing, cuck - oo. now — sing, cuck - oo.   Sing, cuck - oo now — sing, cuck - oo.

bass II

sing, cuck - oo now. — Sing, cuck- oo.   sing, cuck - oo now. —

WE MENTIONED before that songs of indolence comprise an important portion of summer singing. This is a lazy song which recalls the great flatboats that drifted easily down-river with fat cargoes in the days before the railroads. To really "see" this song, one has to imagine the heavy barge gliding down the river while the hot summer sun decorates the ripples with flecks of yellow light.

Down the River

1. The wa-ter is bright and shin-ing like gold, In the rays of the sum-mer sun;___ The
mas-ter is fond of his old Broad-horn, For it brings him plen-ty of tin.___ The
riv-er is deep, the weath-er is fair, The wa-ter it spar-kles like wine.___ The
chan-nel is wide, the course it is set, And___ some-one is sing-ing a song.___ And

cook is be - low, down deep in the hold, A - get - ting the
crew is a - sleep, the car - go is corn, And the mon - ey comes
pace is so slow, we'll nev - er make port, And ev - 'ry - one
don't we have a won - der - ful time, As we go

Chorus

hoe - cakes done. _____
tum - bling in. _____
thinks that it's fine. _____
float - ing a - long. _____

Down the riv - er, down the

riv - er, Down the O - hi - o - hi - o, Down the

riv - er, down the riv - er, Down the O - hi - o; _____

[157]

1.

last time

2. The
3. The
4. The

SOUTHERN STREAMS abound with crayfish, a crustacean which looks like a small, gray lobster, and tastes almost as good. When the summer sun really starts to warm up to its work and the thin little streams dry out, vacationers sometimes find the crayfish scrambling around the muddy banks. The "crawdad" of our song is the same little crustaceous crayfish, but his nickname makes for easier singing.

Crawdad

1. You get a line and I'll get a pole,
2. What're you goin' to do when the stream runs dry,
3. Craw-dad, craw-dad, feel-ing might-y fine,
4. Mud so hot, I could-n't stand still,

hon-ey, _____ You get a line and I'll get a pole, ___
hon-ey? _____ What're you goin' to do when the stream runs dry, ___
hon-ey, _____ Craw-dad, craw-dad, feel-ing might-y fine, ___
hon-ey, _____ Mud so hot, I could-n't stand still, ___

5. Sitting on the bank in the noonday sun, honey,
   Sitting on the bank in the noonday sun, baby,
   Sitting on the bank in the noonday sun;
   Lots of work I won't ever get done—
   Honey, babe o' mine.

INDEPENDENCE DAY

July 4

~§ IN 1776 CONGRESS ADOPTED a declaration written by Thomas Jefferson which recited the repressive acts of George III, declared that these were in opposition to the natural rights of man, and proclaimed the independence of the newly-united states. The general populace was overjoyed by the Declaration, but they had already put their feelings into words and set the words to music in revolutionary songs.

THE COLONISTS not only made up very insulting, inflammatory poems about England, but they went even further. They set their scurrilous words to England's favorite folk songs. Using the music of the British "Derry Down," they sang of a "capitol chop"—revolution—despite the efforts of the British statesmen Chatham, Camden, Barre, Burke, Wilkes, and Glynn to find a compromise.

Derry Down

tent with the Game Act, they tax fish and sea, And Am-er-i-ca drench with hot
that, I be-lieve, is A-mer-i-ca's wish, Since they've drowned us with tea and de-
turn, sure, we Free-men will glad-ly a-gree, To ___ give them a dance on the
fore-fa-thers gave us this free-dom in hand, And we'll die in de-fense of the

Chorus

wa-ter and tea.
prived us of fish. Der-ry down, down, down, der-ry down.
Lib-er-ty Tree.
rights of the land.

2. There's
3. Three
4. Then

ꙮ IN "YANKEE DOODLE," the British made fun of the ragged, rustic, colonial soldiers by imitating the nasal New England twang. In return, the American troops composed their own lampoon, making fun of the British uniform (too gaudy), the British accent (too clipped), and the British penchant for retreating under Yankee fire.

The Old Soldiers
of the King

sing you a song, (as a po-et might say,) Of King Geor-ge's old
hearts bid us stand, and our heads bid us stay, But our legs were strong-
great ex-pe-di-tion cost in-fi-nite sums, But some un-der-paid
fight one an-oth-er that way if they please, But we don't have to

Chorus

sol-diers who ne'er run a-way.
mind-ed and took us a-way. We're the old sol-diers of the King, And the
dood-les, they cut us to crumbs.
stand for such tac-tics as these.

King's own reg-u-lars._____ 2. At
3. To ___
4. They

5. We turned and we ran, but that doesn't disgrace us—
   We did it to prove that the foe could not face us.
   And they've naught to brag of, be sure that's the case,
   Though we lost in the fight, we came first in the race.
   CHORUS

[167]

IN 1776 THE IDEA of a revolution was revolutionary. No one had ever heard of such an unheard-of affair. King George III was furious and immediately set about raising an army to punish the ungrateful colonists. Some of the soldiers who sailed to America stayed to become good American citizens. We don't know what happened to the man who wrote this song, but the song, at least, has settled in this country comfortably.

The Wicked Rebels

1. On the ninth day of No-vem-ber, At the
   sailed a - way to New York, We at
(2.) mourn - ful was the part - ing Of the
      no one knew for sar - tin They'd re-

dawn - ing in the sky, Ere we mead - ows fair of Kings - bridge, How the
an - chor here did lie. O'er the wom - en were a - weep - ing And they
sol - diers and their wives, For that
turn home with their lives. All the

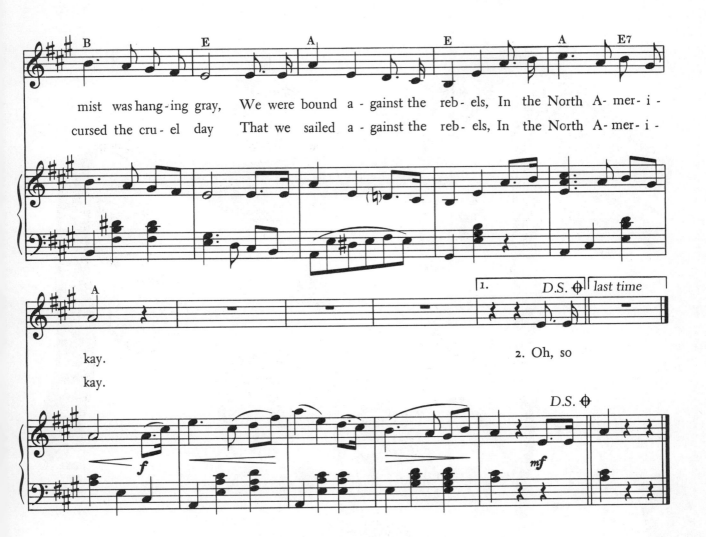

mist was hang-ing gray, We were bound a - gainst the reb - els, In the North A- mer- i -
cursed the cru - el day That we sailed a - gainst the reb - els, In the North A- mer- i -

kay.
kay.

2. Oh, so

3. All the little babes were holding Out their arms with saddest cries,
   And the bitter tears were falling From their pretty, simple eyes,
   That their scarlet-coated daddies Must be hastening away
   For to fight the wicked rebels, In the North Amerikay.

4. Now, with "God preserve our monarch," Let us finish up our strain,
   Be his subjects ever loyal, And his honor all maintain.
   May the Lord our voyage prosper, And our arms across the sea,
   And put down the wicked rebels, In the North Amerikee.

LABOR DAY

First Monday in September

᠊ᣥ IN OUR COUNTRY we have no "Management Day," or "White-Collar Day," or "Government Official Day." The first Monday in September, originally set aside to include all working people, now is considered a holiday for doctors, lawyers, teachers, foremen, dowsers, and other specialists. It's one of the few holidays which is celebrated in every state and territory.

WHENEVER OUR NATION is threatened by some disaster—war, flood, epidemic, or depression—working men and women join hands to work for the good of all. Of course, it's the combined efforts of people in all professions which make our nation so powerful in peacetime, but our first song for Labor Day dates from the War of 1812. It tells of the volunteers who dug the fortifications designed to prevent the British Army from capturing the city of Philadelphia.

The Patriotic Diggers

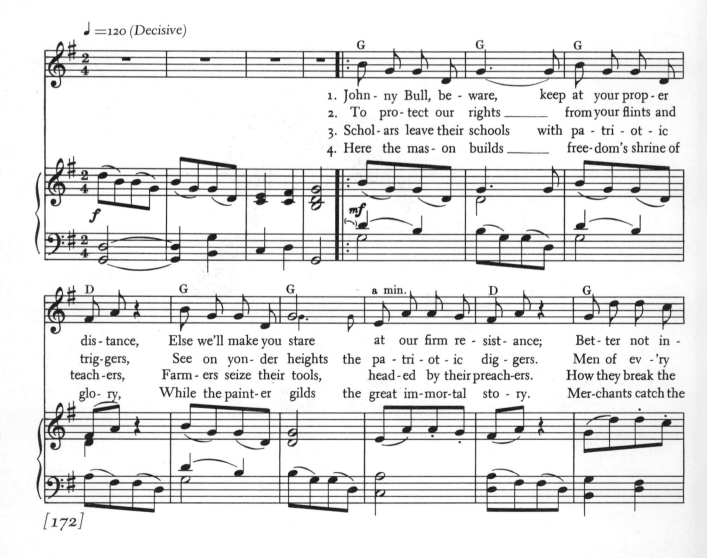

♩=120 (Decisive)

1. John - ny Bull, be - ware,   keep at your prop - er
2. To pro - tect our rights ____   from your flints and
3. Schol - ars leave their schools   with pa - tri - ot - ic
4. Here the mas - on builds ____   free - dom's shrine of

dis - tance,   Else we'll make you stare   at our firm re - sist - ance;   Bet - ter not in -
trig - gers,   See on yon - der heights   the pa - tri - ot - ic dig - gers.   Men of ev - 'ry
teach - ers,   Farm - ers seize their tools,   head - ed by their preach - ers.   How they break the
glo - ry,   While the paint - er gilds   the great im - mor - tal sto - ry.   Mer - chants catch the

vade, re - col - lect the spir - it Which our dads dis- played, and their sons in -
age,   col - or, rank, pro- fes - sion, Ar - dent- ly en - gaged, la - bor in suc-
soil, brew-ers,butch-ers, bak - ers; Here the doc- tors toil, there, the un-der-
flame, toi - lers feel the spir - it All will share the fame. all de- serve the

last time

her - it.
ces - sion.
tak - ers.
cred - it.

⊸§ YOU MAY BE surprised to learn that "The Levee Song" is that old work horse of the folk song stable, "I've Been Working On the Railroad." It's one of our most useful songs, having been sung as "I've Been Working on the Erie," "I've Been Working On the Prairie," and so forth. The work gangs that built our railroads, highways, and levees usually labored under one captain, and usually ate food prepared by one cook. In the morning the whistle would blow, the cook would sound the breakfast horn, and the men would sit down to eat while the captain fretted with impatience.

The Levee Song

all the live - long day. _____ I've been work - ing on the lev - ee, to

pass the time a - way. _____ Can't you hear the whis - tle blow - ing,

"Rise up so ear - ly in the morn?" _____ Can't you hear the cap - tain shout - ing,

Some - one's in the kitch - en, I know, I know, _____
fee, _____ fi, _____ fid - dle - ee - i - o, i o, _____

Some - one's in the kitch - en with Di - nah,
Fee, _____ fi, _____ fid - dle - ee - i - o,

Strum - ming on the old ban - jo. Sing - ing jo.

3. All I want from this creation, working on the levee.
   A pretty gal with a big plantation, working on the levee.
   CHORUS

4. Wish a bushel, wish a peck, working on the levee.
   Wish a gal around my neck, working on the levee.
   CHORUS

❧ AMERICANS HAVE created their own private musical form known as "The Blues." It uses a syncopated beat, flatted third and seventh notes, and a generous application of daily sentiments and common expressions. Sometimes, the singer will express sentiments in the blues that he wouldn't dare use in ordinary conversation.

We'll All Work Together

1. Work - ing on the rail - road, work - ing in the mine,
2. Work - ing in the weave room, work - ing all the day,
3. Cap - tain got a time - clock, some - thing wrong with it,
4. Ev - 'ry Sun - day morn - ing, loaf - ing like a bum,

No one's ham - mer ev - er ring like mine.
Hours get - ting long - er but I'm get - ting short - er pay.
Fast - er in the morn - ing, slow - er 'fore we quit.
Spend the day a - wish - ing Mon - day nev - er come.

Chorus
And we'll

CONSTITUTION DAY

 "We, the people of the United States, in order to form a more perfect Union, establish justice, insure domestic tranquillity, provide for the common defense, promote the general welfare, and secure the blessings of liberty to ourselves and our posterity, do ordain and establish this Constitution for the United States of America." That's the way our Constitution begins, and, together with the later amendments known as the Bill of Rights, it helped insure the liberty we've always prized.

FOLLOWING THE CUSTOMARY practice of appropriating British songs for anti-British verses, the American poet John Dickinson used an English navy song, "Hearts of Oak," for his revolutionary sentiments. This song was probably the first popular propaganda piece that spoke up for colonial rights. It appeared in 1768 and foresaw the day when the pursuit of liberty might mean war.

In Freedom We're Born

1. Come, join hand in hand, brave A -
   join hand in hand, brave A -

mon - ey we'll give.

2. Then

WHEN GEORGE WASHINGTON was inaugurated in New York City, the band played a new march composed especially for the occasion. Nine years later, England and France were at war and Americans were wrangling and taking sides in the conflict. A gentle poet named John Hopkinson wrote words to "The Inaugural March" suggesting subtly that Americans should stay united, mind their own business, and keep busy protecting the United States Constitution.

Hail, Columbia

1. Hail, Co - lum - bia, hap - py land! Hail, ye he - roes, heav'n-born band, Who
2. Im - mor - tal pa - triots! rise once more, De - fend your rights, de - fend your shore, Let

fought and bled in Free - dom's cause, Who fought and bled in Free - dom's_cause, And
no rude foe with im - pious_hand, Let no rude foe with im - pious_hand, In -

when the storm of war was gone, En - joyed the peace your
vade the shrine where sa - cred lies Of toil and blood the

val - or won. Let in - de - pend - ence be our boast,
well - earn'd prize. While of - fering peace, sin - cere and just,

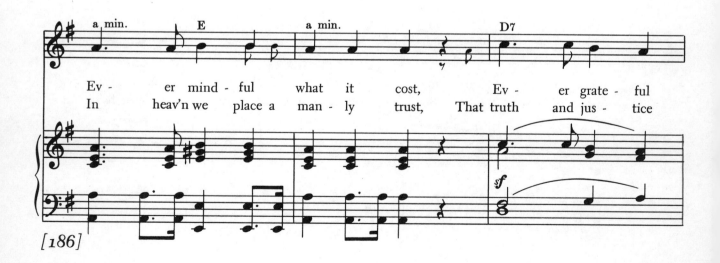

Ev - er mind - ful what it cost, Ev - er grate - ful
In heav'n we place a man - ly trust, That truth and jus - tice

[186]

for __ the __ prize   Let   its   al - tar   reach   the   skies.
will __ pre - vail   And   ev'- ry   scheme   of   bond - age   fail.

Chorus
Firm, u - nit - ed,   let __ us __ be,   Rally-ing   round our   lib - er - ty.

As   a   band of __ broth - ers __ joined, __   Peace __ and __ safe - ty   we   shall   find.

IN 1798 THE Alien and Sedition Acts were passed. These penalized anyone who might utter false, scandalous, or malicious words against the government. Americans, jealous of their right to criticize, objected very strongly. Thomas Jefferson was elected President in 1801 and immediately pardoned all those imprisoned under the unpopular Acts. To the tune of a Scottish reel, the grateful populace sang this song.

Jefferson and Liberty

♩. = 100-104 (Lilting)

1. The gloom - y night __ be - fore us flies, The
   lord - lings here __ with gorg - ing jaws, Shall
   stran - gers from __ a thou - sand shores, Com-

reign of ter - ror now __ is o'er, __ No gags, in - quis - i -
wring from in - dus - try __ the food, __ No big - ots, with their
pelled by tyr - an - ny __ to roam, __ Shall find, a - midst a -

2. No
3. Here,

AUTUMN

For many Americans (which is what authors usually say when they want to express their personal opinions) autumn is the loveliest time of the year. The leaves blaze with colors no artist can paint, the air is crisp and clear, and the harvest moon shines with a soft, mellow light over most of our countryside.

THE COMING OF autumn sends happy students back to school and their studies. To commemorate this joyous occasion, we've a song which grew up on the southern plantations, where many unfortunate children sang about the school they never were able to visit. On the words, "Ha, Ha, Thisaway," bend to the left; on, "Ha, Ha, Thataway," bend to the right. On "Then, Oh, Then," clap your hands once for each word. It may seem silly, but it's good exercise.

Ha, Ha, Thisaway

1. When I was a lit-tle boy,
   Dad-dy came and got __ me,

2. I went in-to the school there,
   Learned the Gold-en Rule __ there,

lit-tle old lit-tle boy, When I was a lit-tle boy, five years old,
came __ and got __ me, Dad-dy did-n't scold __ me, I've been told.
lit-tle old school __ there, Went in-to the school __ there, school so old;
lit-tle old rule __ there, Learned the Gold-en Rule __ there, I've been told.

Ha, ha, this-a-way; Ha, ha, that-a-way; Ha, ha, this-a-way

Then, oh, then.

3. Learned my lesson, little old lesson,
   Learned my lesson like I was told.
   Wasn't that a blessing, little old blessing?
   Learned my lesson, at five years old.

4. Met my teacher, little old teacher,
   Met my teacher, he didn't scold.
   Said, "I'm glad to meetcha, meetcha, meetcha,"
   Said, "I'm glad to meetcha," like I was told.

Indian Summer is that lazy time in autumn when everything seems so wonderful we wish that the clocks would all slow down to a lazy crawl. The harvest moon is red in the sky and the birds, having practiced through the spring and summer, are busy singing their finest songs. Red shirts are seen in the woods as hunters fire their guns at forest animals and other hunters. Our autumn hunting song comes from England where it was sung as "The Chareful Harn," with the refrain "and wale a-huntin' gao."

The Cheerful Horn

1. The cheer - ful horn, it cheer - ful horn, it
2. here's a toast to here's a toast to
blows in the morn, And we'll a - hunt - ing go. The
blows in the morn, And we'll a - hunt - ing go.
our dear host, And to our host - ess, too. Then
our dear host, And to our host - ess, too,

And we'll a-hunt-ing go____ And we'll a-hunt-ing go.____ For

all my fan-cy dwells up-on Nan-cy, I'll sing "Tal-ly Ho." For Ho." 2. Then

As the leaves begin to fall on the still summer-warm earth, the corn ripens to the point when it's ready for the shucking. The harvest must be brought in before the winter comes on, and it's accomplished with a spirit of rejoicing. This is displayed in hay rides, barn dances, and corn shuckings. The fellow who shucks a red ear of corn is allowed, even encouraged, to kiss any girl he wishes. Often this leaves the girl's cheeks redder than the corn.

The Shucking of the Corn

1. The sun shines down on the corn - field,
   I had a ship on the o - cean,
   corn is red on the corn - stalks,

The
All
The

moon is wait - ing to shine. Be - fore I'd let my
lad - en with sil - ver and gold, Be - fore I'd let my
leaves are red on the tree, And I'll be true to

Chorus

true love go, I'd work through the win - ter time.
true love suf - fer, The ship and its car - go would be sold.
my true love, If she will be true to me. I'm a-

going to the shuck - ing of the corn, I'm a-

going to the shuck - ing of the corn, The

shuck - ing of the corn and the blow - ing of the horn, I'm a -

go - ing to the shuck- ing of the corn. 2. If corn.
3. The

last time

COLUMBUS DAY

October 12

§ ONLY THIRTY-FIVE states celebrate Columbus Day. It's ironic that the great navigator is denied full recognition today just as he was denied it in his native Genoa, in England, in Portugal, and, for many years, even in Spain. It is true that our nation is sometimes called "Columbia," but officially the continent is named after Amerigo Vespucci, one of Columbus's chief competitors.

IN HIS NATIVE ITALY, the great explorer was named "Cristoforo Colombo." In Spain, his name was given as "Cristobal Colon." In America, we call him "Christopher Columbus." It's no wonder, therefore, that some people mix the names up, and in this song call him "Christopher Columbo." However, there're very few excuses for the feeble humor expressed in the verses, and so we make very few excuses.

Christopher Columbo

♩. =108 (Gaily)

1. In

four - teen hun - dred nine - ty- two, Three ships set out to sea; The
sailed a - way from Ge - no - ay; No soon - er did they sail, When
met the Queen of Spain and said, "Just give me ships and car - go; And
crew went mad and mu - ti - nied, They drew their dirks and gat - lings; Co -

Nin - a one, the Pin - ta, two, The third, the San - ta Mar - ie.
half the crew and of - fi - cers Turned green a - long __ the rail.
hang me up un - til I'm dead If I don't bring back __ Chi - ca - go."
lum - bus took a mar - lin spike And chased them up __ the rat - lines.

Chorus

He said the world was round-o, A - mer - i - ca he found-o, The

cal - cu - lat - ing, nav - i - gat - ing Chris - to - pher Co - lum-bo.

1.
last time
2. They
3. He lum-bo.
4. The

[201]

Columbus was not an amateur. Before voyaging to America, he had already traveled to England, Iceland, the Guinea coast, and the Greek Islands, and he had studied navigation and astronomy at the University of Pavia in Italy. But the charts of the day showed only dragons and sea monsters on the unexplored edge of the ocean, and only a voyage could satisfy his curiosity. Despite the first line of the song, he was an expert at "boxing the compass."

Sailing on the Sea

♩=66 (Gaily)

1. Chris - to - pher Co - lum - bus did - n't have a com - pass,
2. Chris - to - pher Co - lum - bus did - n't have a com - pass,
3. Chris - to - pher Co - lum - bus did - n't have a com - pass,

Did - n't have a bin - na - cle as he sailed a - long. Though the day was
Did - n't have an en - gin - eer as he sailed a - long. O - cean-go - ing
Did - n't have a life - boat as he sailed a - long. So the crew got

windy,   swore he'd reach the Ind - ies,   But   he reached A - mer - i - ca,
breez - es   tore the sail to piec - es,   Still   he reached A - mer - i - ca,
fran - tic   on the deep At - lan - tic,   But   he reached A - mer - i - ca,

so   we sing this song.
so   we sing this song.   Hail   to Co - lum - bus, did - n't have a com - pass,
so   we sing this song.

Sail - ing mer - ry,   fast, and free,   Sail - ing on the sea.

◈§ COLUMBUS'S DISCOVERIES meant that Spain would have enough riches to enable her to stand among the foremost nations of the world. Cortes and Pizarro conquered the American Indians and sent cargoes of gold and silver back to the motherland. By 1590, Spain was strong enough to arm an Armada against England. The British retaliated in force and their Grand Fleet defeated the Spaniards. When recalled to England, the sailors made up a song in which, like Columbus's crew, they bid farewell to the fair Spanish ladies.

The Spanish Ladies

la - dies of Spain. For __ we've re - ceived or - ders to
on the salt sea, Un - til we strike sound - ings in the
sound - ing did take; 'Twas __ for - ty - five fath - oms with a

sail for old Eng - land, But we hope in a short time to be
chan - nel of Eng - land, From __ U - shant to Scil - ly is __
white sand - y bot - tom, So we squared up the main - yard and up -

with you a - gain.
for - ty - five leagues.
wind we did make.

2. We'll
3. We

[205]

HALLOWEEN

October 31

⊰§ THE EVE of All Hallows, or All Saints' Day, is called "Hallow E'en." The superstitious used to believe that goblins, fairies, witches, and ghosts appeared on this night, but things have changed. Now it's a time for telling ghost stories, bobbing for disenchanted apples, and looking into mirrors with the hope of seeing someone else's face reflected therein.

HERE's A GHOST STORY that won't frighten anyone. It may once have been a true story and a melancholy song but, as we pointed out earlier, things have changed. As in other formerly fearful and tearful folk songs, a ridiculous chorus and a hopping melody prevent us from getting too miserable when faced with the damp ghost of the courageous fisherman.

The Bold Fisherman

♩.=56 (Humorously)

1. There was a bold fish-er-man who sailed out from Pim-li-co, To slew the wild cod-fish and the bold mack-er-

wrig-gled and scrig-gled in the wa-ter so brin-y-o, He yel-loed and bel-lowed for help, but in

ghost walked at mid-night to the side of his Mar-y Jane. When he told her how dead he was, she took it right

al.   But when he got to Pim - li - co, the storm - y winds did
vain;   Then down - ward he did gent - ly slide to the bot - tom of the
bad.   "Oh, since my love is gone," said she, "All joy on earth has

wild - ly blow; His lit - tle boat went wib - ble - wob - ble, and o - ver - board went
o - cean tide, But pre - vi - ous to this he cried,__ "Fare thee well, Mar - y
fled for me; I nev - er more shall hap - py be." __ And she went rav - ing

he.   **Chorus** Sing - ing twink - ee - dood - le - um, twink - ee - dood - le - um. 'Twas a
Jane."
mad.

high - ly in - te - res - ting song he sung: Twink - ee - dood - le - um,

twink - ee - dood - le - um, Sang the bold fish - er - man.

1.
last time

2. He
3. His

IN SEARCHING FOR Halloween songs, many a ghostly subject comes to mind. Visitations and vampires appear in innumerable ballads. This song is one of the music hall creations of the 1890's. Aside from its crystal clear poetry, it boasts one of the most original ghosts of all time. It also mentions the "Fire Zou-Zous," the same colorful soldiers that figured in our singing of "Abraham's Daughter."

The Peanut Stand

1. Come, lis - ten to me close - ly, While I re - hearse a dit - ty, It's all a - bout a
Bid - dy Mc - Ghee was a fine young girl, And not - ed near and far;__ Kept a pea - nut stand in
Con - nie O' Ryan was a fine young boy, And not - ed far and near,__ He could meet the champ at
Bid - dy Mc - Ghee she heard the news, She took right to her bed.__ Her moth - er kept Con - nie from

[211]

fair young girl Who lived in Jer- sey Cit- y. She fell in love with a
Jer- sey to Sup- ply the rail- road car.___ But when her moth-er met___
bowl- ing and He'd beat him free and clear.___ But he fell in with a par-cel of___
com-ing a - round, So the poor girl died right dead.___ Her death took ef- fect on___

bright young lad Who was hand-some in his prime; He was chief en- gi- neer of a
Con-nie O' Ryan, She___ did not like his clan, And she said if her daugh-ter kept
New York toughs, And they led him a-round like a toy; And he joined the ___ New York ___
Con-nie, poor lad, And he nev-er could march in time, So ___ out of the Corps in a

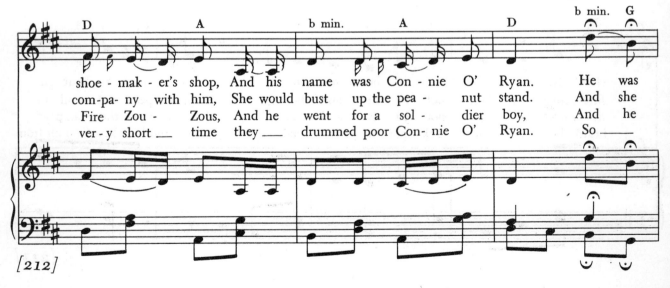

shoe- mak- er's shop, And his name was Con- nie O' Ryan. He was
com-pa- ny with him, She would bust up the pea- nut stand. And she
Fire Zou- Zous, And he went for a sol- dier boy, And he
ver- y short ___ time they ___ drummed poor Con- nie O' Ryan. So ___

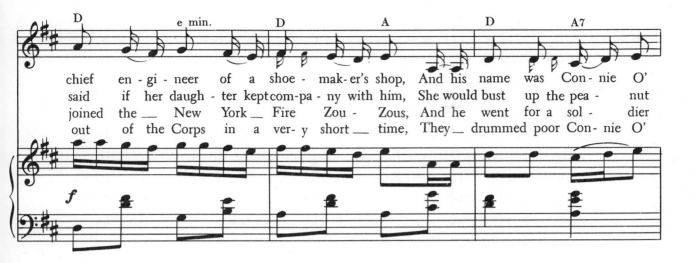

chief en - gi - neer of a shoe - mak - er's shop, And his name was Con - nie O'
said if her daugh - ter kept com-pa - ny with him, She would bust up the pea - nut
joined the __ New York __ Fire Zou - Zous, And he went for a sol - dier
out of the Corps in a ver- y short __ time, They __ drummed poor Con- nie O'

Ryan.   2. Now,
stand.   3. Now,
boy.   4. When
Ryan.   5. The

5. The old woman's house is haunted now.
Every night about twelve o'clock
She sees a remarkable kind of a sight,
Which gives her a horrible shock!
It's the ghosts of Connie and Biddy McGhee,
Come a-walking hand in hand,
And right behind them, a-marching along,
Is the ghost of the peanut stand.
And right behind them, a-marching along,
Is the ghost of the peanut stand.

[213]

❧ IN FOLKLORE, the Devil often appears suddenly and tries to pick up a few souls on his way to Perdition. One of his tricks is to ask a series of difficult riddles. If the victim gives the wrong answers, he is stuffed unceremoniously into the Devil's knapsack and given a free ride into the everlasting flames. In this song, fortunately, the young lady or gentleman knew the proper responses and escaped with his soul intact, though smelling slightly of brimstone.

The Devil's Nine Questions

♩.=63-66 (Simply)

1. Oh, you must an-swer my ques-tions nine, Sing nine - ty- nine and
   what is whit-er ___ than the milk? Sing nine - ty- nine and
   snow is whit-er ___ than the milk, Sing nine ty- nine and
   what is high-er ___ than the tree? Sing nine - ty- nine and

nine-ty, Or you're not God's___ but one of mine, And you're not the weav - ers
nine-ty, And what is soft - er than the silk? And you're not the weav - ers
nine-ty, And down is soft - er than the silk, And we are the weav - ers
nine-ty, And what is deep - er than the sea? And you're not the weav - ers

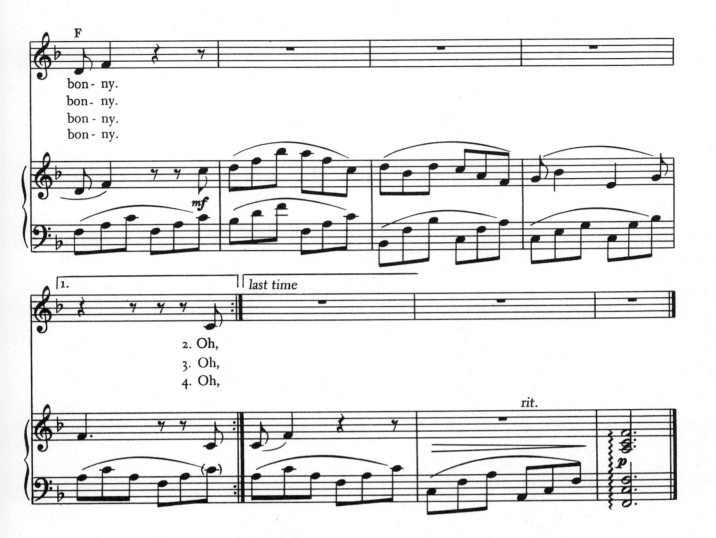

bon - ny.
bon - ny.
bon - ny.
bon - ny.

1.

last time

2. Oh,
3. Oh,
4. Oh,

rit.

5. Oh, Heav'n is higher than the tree,
   Sing ninety-nine and ninety,
   And Hell is deeper than the sea,
   And we are the weavers bonny.

6. Oh, what is louder than a horn?
   Sing ninety-nine and ninety,
   And what is sharper than a thorn?
   And you're not the weavers bonny.

7. Oh, thunder is louder than a horn,
   Sing ninety-nine and ninety,
   And hunger is sharper than a thorn,
   And we are the weavers bonny.

8. Oh, what is wicked man's repay?
   Sing ninety-nine and ninety,
   And what is longer than the way?
   And you're not the weavers bonny.

9. Oh, Hell is wicked man's repay,
   Sing ninety-nine and ninety,
   And love is longer than the way,
   And we are the weavers bonny.

10. Oh, what is redder than the wine?
    Sing ninety-nine and ninety,
    And now you've heard my questions nine,
    And you're not the weavers bonny.

11. Oh, blood is redder than the wine,
    Sing ninety-nine and ninety,
    And now we've answered your questions nine,
    And we are the weavers bonny.

12. Yes, you have answered my questions nine,
    Sing ninety-nine and ninety,
    And you are God's, you're none of mine,
    And you are the weavers bonny.

ELECTION DAY

*Tuesday after the first
Monday in November*

THERE IS a story about a man who was asked by an overly inquisitive stranger, "How did you vote in the last election?" His answer was, "By secret ballot." The wonderful right which we enjoy every year isn't shared by most other nations. It's a right earned by men who fought bitterly to gain it and keep it. Some of our folk songs reflect this anxious desire to keep the ballot forever free.

EVERY ONCE in a great while some community hears one candidate charge that his rival has tampered with the ballots. This is one of the most serious charges that can be brought against a citizen. It's almost impossible to tamper with a mechanical voting machine, but in the old days of paper ballots it was much easier and very tempting to unpopular candidates. In 1848, this song was written on the subject to the tune of "Yankee Doodle."

Fair and Free Elections

1. While some on rights and some on wrongs, Pre-fer their own re-flec-tions, The peo-ple's right must still be strong, The right to free e-lec-tions.

2. E-lec-tions are to make our laws, For trade, peace, and pro-tec-tion; Who fails to vote, for-sakes the cause Of fair and free e-lec-tions.

3. The peo-ple speak, they must be heard, Their voice must be as-cend-ant; The can-di-date must heed the word, And on it be de-pend-ent.

4. Each town and coun-ty's wealth and peace, Its trade and all con-nec-tions, With art and sci-ence must in-crease, By fair and free e-lec-tions.

Law and or - der be the stake, With free- dom in se - lec - tion. Let all stand by the

 bal - lot - box, For fair and free e - lec - tion.

5. Should enemies beset our land
   With traitor's disaffections,
   Undaunted, we will stand our ground,
   Upheld by free elections.
       CHORUS:

American Campaign Songs

CAMPAIGN SONGS have usually been written to the melody of popular favorites in order to ensure that the audience would sing along. "Yankee Doodle" has carried the words on many occasions. When Lincoln ran, the words were:

> *Lincoln came to Washington*
> *To view the situation;*
> *He found the White House upside down,*
> *And rumpus in the nation.*

And Garfield's song was:

> *The soldier boys are wide awake,*
> *And eager for the fray, sirs!*
> *They'll vote for Garfield, no mistake,*
> *Come next election day, sirs!*

The hero of the Battle of Tippecanoe was General William Henry Harrison. When he ran for office, with Tyler as his Vice President, his campaign song used as its melody, "Auld Lang Syne":

> *Van Buren is a used-up man,*
> *Hurrah for Tippecanoe.*
> *And surely he will get your vote,*
> *And so will Tyler, too.*
> *For old Tippecanoe, my lads,*
> *For old Tippecanoe,*
> *We'll vote him to the White House, lads,*
> *And we'll vote for Tyler, too.*

William Henry Harrison's grandson, Benjamin Harrison, ran for the Presidency against Grover Cleveland. Cleveland's song, to the tune of "Grandfather's Clock," intimated that Harrison wasn't the man his grandfather had been:

> *His grandfather's hat is too big for his head,*
> *But Ben tries it on just the same.*
> *It fits him too quick, which has oft-times been said,*
> *With regard to his grandfather's fame.*

It was bought long ago and it makes a pretty show
In this jolly hard cider campaign,
But it won't fit, even a little bit,
On Benjamin Harrison's brain.

In answer to this biting satire, the Harrison forces merely chanted:

Grover, Grover, all is over,
Grover, Grover, all is over.

Cleveland's supporters answered with another rhythmic call, a plea that Cleveland be returned to office:

Four, four, four years more,
Four, four, four years more.

Zachary Taylor was a brave general in the Mexican War. When he was a candidate for President, his cohorts reminded the voters of his bravery in the field, to the tune of "Old Dan Tucker":

They met us on the Rio Grandy,
We played them Yankee Doodle Dandy.
When Old Zack Taylor crossed the line,
He made them snort like a steam engyne.
Rumadum dum, we'll vote for Taylor,
Rumadum dum, the son of Freedom,
Rumadum dum, we'll vote for Taylor,
He's the boy can skin and beat 'em.

The Presidents

HERE'S A SONG which can be used as a mnemonic device for those who can't remember such vital facts as the capitals of the states, the population figures of all cities on the 45th parallel, or the names and deeds of the Presidents. This is the time to learn the names of the Presidents because in years to come there'll be new names, making the work more difficult. This song, to the tune of "Yankee Doodle," has been brought up to date as the result of back-breaking research and skillful rhyming.

George Washington, first president, by Adams was succeeded,
And Thomas Jefferson was next, the people's cause he pleaded.
James Madison, he then came forth, to give John Bull a peeling,
And James Monroe was next to go in the era of good feeling.

'Twas John Q. Adams then came in and, after, Andrew Jackson,
Who licked the British at New Orleans with much great satisfaction.
Van Buren then was next to chair and Harrison and Tyler—
The latter made the Whigs so mad they almost burst their b'iler.

We next elected James K. Polk, the worse that then did vex us
Was, should we fight with Mexico and take in Lone Star Texas.
Then Taylor was our leader, but he soon had to forsake it,
For Millard Fillmore filled it more; Frank Pierce then said, "I'll take it."

James Buchanan next popped right in and Lincoln then was chosen,
Who found the problems of the day were anything but frozen.
And Johnson had a rougher time, the Senate would impeach him,
But as it took a two-thirds vote, they lacked one vote to reach him.

And then we came to U. S. Grant, who made his name at Shiloh;
Then Hayes, and Garfield, who got shot, they both hailed from Ohio.
Chet Arthur then the scepter held till Cleveland took it over,
Ben Harrison got sandwiched in, for once more it was Grover.

McKinley kindled Spain to war and Teddy Roosevelt fought it.
Then Teddy took the White House key, till William H. Taft sought it.
Next Wilson kept us out of war until we had to win it;
He tried to get us in the League, but we saw nothing in it.

The next was Warren Harding with his Teapot Dome a-boiling,
Till Coolidge took the kettle off, in silence ever toiling.
The boom came in with Hoover, but it very soon got busted,
And Franklin Roosevelt got the call and four times was entrusted.

The Axis started World War Two and fought till they got meager,
When Roosevelt died and Truman came, he didn't seem too eager.
But still he ran and fought against the Communistic power,
Until the G.O.P. rode back and won with Eisenhower.

VETERANS DAY

November 11

WHEN WORLD WAR I was over, the people of the world prayed that it had truly been "the war to end all wars." But the "Armistice" turned out to be just what its Latin root implies, a space between the hostilities. It seemed wasteful to set aside a day to celebrate peace where there was no peace, and so November 11th was changed from "Armistice Day" to "Veterans Day." Nevertheless, we always greet November 11th with the hope that the "space between the hostilities" will be an everlasting one.

"WHEN THE WAR is over we will all enlist again; in a blue moon, boys, we will." So sang the soldiers of World War II. Some of their songs complained of the dangers of warfare, but most concentrated on minor annoyances. These have been the same since war began: ill-fitting clothes, poisonous food (and not enough of it), low wages, and the lack of female companionship.

Gee, Mom, I Want to Go Home

1. They tell you in the Ar-my, The cof-fee's might-y fine, It's good for cuts and bruis-es, It
2. The bis-cuits that they give us, They say are might-y fine; Well, one fell off the tab-le, And
3. The cloth-ing that they give us, They say is might-y fine; Me and half my reg-i-ment, Can
4. The girls down at the serv-ice club, They say are might-y fine; Half are o-ver eight-y, And the

tastes like tur - pen - tine.
crushed a pal of mine.
all fit in - to mine.
rest are un - der nine.

Chorus

I don't want no more of Ar - my life;

Gee, Mom, I want to go home.

5. The salary they pay us,
   They say is mighty fine;
   They pay you fifty dollars,
   And they take back sixty-nine.
       CHORUS

6. They tell you in the mess-hall,
   The chicken's mighty fine,
   But one fell off the table,
   And it started marking time.
       CHORUS

THIS SONG was written down by Patrick Gilmore, bandmaster of the Union Army during the War Between the States. In Ireland, it was sung as a slow, sad wail, and told of a returning soldier badly wounded in the wars. Americans know it as a sprightly, joyous welcome to the conquering hero.

When Johnny Comes Marching Home

rah,_____ hur-rah;_____ The men will cheer,__ the boys will shout, The la - dies, they_ will
rah,_____ hur-rah;_____ The vil - lage lads__ and las - sies say, With ros - es they_ will
rah,_____ hur-rah;_____ The laur - el wreath__ is read - y now, To place up- on __ his

all turn out; And we'll all feel gay When John- ny comes march-ing home. __ 2.The
strew the way; And we'll all feel gay When John- ny comes march-ing home. __ 3.Get
loy - al brow; And we'll all feel gay When John- ny comes march-ing

last time

home. _____

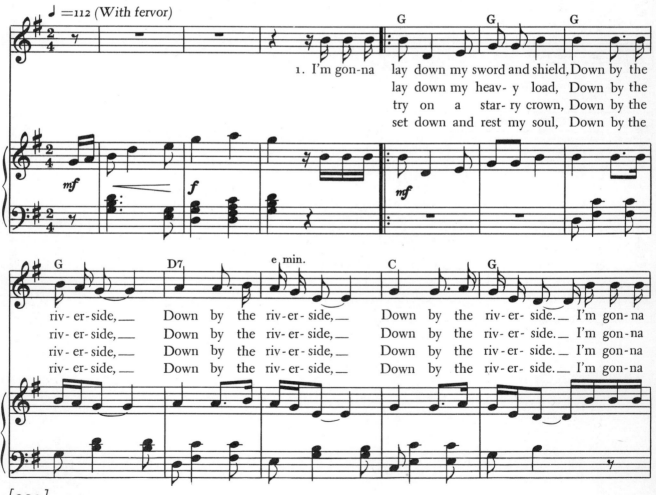

As THE MOMENT of cease-fire approaches, the soldier begins to count the hours. "If I can only hold out another day . . . another hour . . . another minute . . . ten seconds to go. . . ." When the moment of peace arrives and the guns are still, all the soldier wants to do is take off his uniform, put down his rifle, and enjoy the blessings of peace and freedom. This spiritual has captured every man's deep desire for a quiet life and spiritual repose.

Down by the Riverside

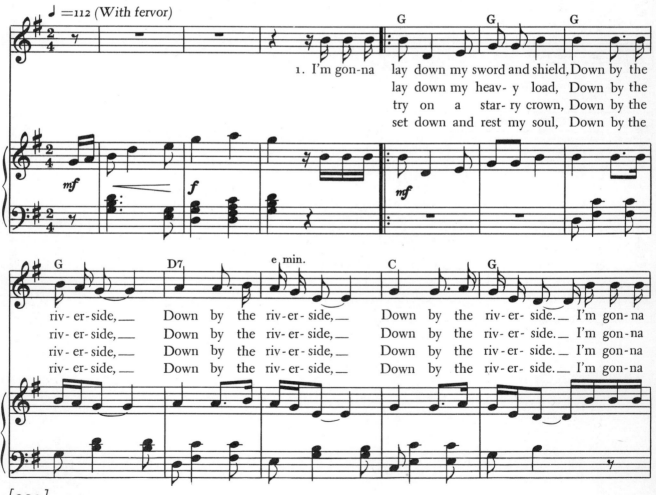

♩=112 (With fervor)

1. I'm gon-na lay down my sword and shield, Down by the
lay down my heav-y load, Down by the
try on a star-ry crown, Down by the
set down and rest my soul, Down by the

riv-er-side,— Down by the riv-er-side,— Down by the riv-er-side.— I'm gon-na
riv-er-side,— Down by the riv-er-side,— Down by the riv-er-side.— I'm gon-na
riv-er-side,— Down by the riv-er-side,— Down by the riv-er-side.— I'm gon-na
riv-er-side,— Down by the riv-er-side,— Down by the riv-er-side.— I'm gon-na

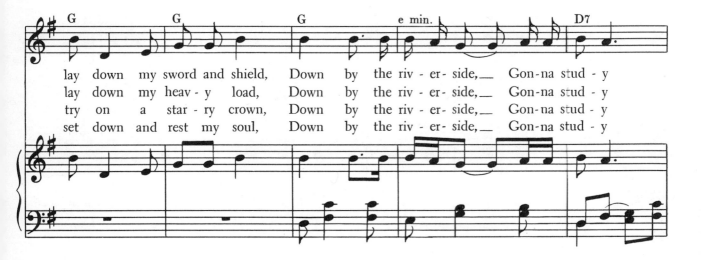

lay down my sword and shield, Down by the riv-er-side,— Gon-na stud-y
lay down my heav-y load, Down by the riv-er-side,— Gon-na stud-y
try on a star-ry crown, Down by the riv-er-side,— Gon-na stud-y
set down and rest my soul, Down by the riv-er-side,— Gon-na stud-y

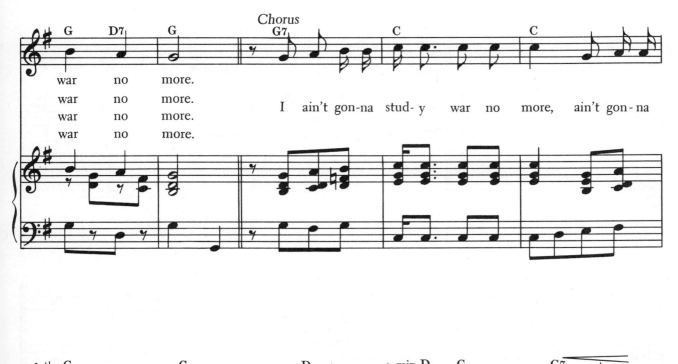

Chorus

war no more.
war no more.
war no more.   I ain't gon-na stud-y war no more, ain't gon-na
war no more.

stud-y war no more, ain't gon-na stud-y — war no more._____ I ain't gon-na

stud - y   war   no   more,   ain't gon-na stud - y   war   no   more,   ain't gon-na stud-y

war   no   more.

1.   last time

2. I'm gon-na
3. I'm gon-na
4. I'm gon-na

THANKSGIVING DAY

By Presidential Proclamation

THE PILGRIMS were deeply religious. Through the storms on the Atlantic and the starvation days that followed their landing on Plymouth Rock, they never forgot to give thanks to God for the small comforts they were able to find. When they finally carved a home in the wilderness with the help of friendly Indians, they looked at their harvest and decided that a special thanks-giving was in order. It was the year 1621, and we've been following their example ever since.

SETTLERS FROM HOLLAND were among the first colonists to the New World. They left us few songs for our folk music collection, but we do have one Dutch hymn which is a Thanksgiving regular. It's as familiar as the turkey and cranberry sauce that help round out the holiday. We sing a version of the Netherlands hymn which was translated into English by Doctor Theodore Baker.

Hymn of Thanksgiving

♩=104 (Smoothly)

mf

f

D   D   A7   D   A   E   A

1. We gath- er to- geth- er to ask the Lord's bles- sing, He hast- ens and chast- ens His
all do ex- tol thee, Thou Lead- er in bat- tle, And pray that Thou still our de-
side us to guide us, our God with us join- ing, Or- dain- ing, main- tain- ing His

will   to make known. The   wick - ed op - pres - sing, cease them ___ from dis -
fend - er wilt be. Let   Thy   con - gre - ga - tion es -   cape ___ trib - u -
King - dom Di - vine. So,   from   the be - gin - ning, the   fight ___ we were

tres- sing, Sing   prais - es to His name, ___ He for - gets not His own. 2.We
la - tion;   Thy   name   be ev- er prais - ed, O ___ Lord, make us free. 3. Be -
win - ning, Thou, Lord,   wast at our side, ___ the ___ glo - ry   be   Thine.

col 8va ad lib. – – – – – – – – – – – – – – – – – – –

§ OUR ONLY NATIVE Americans, the Indians, have been treated rather harshly by motion pictures and other entertainment media. It's surprising that the Indian was so docile when the first immigrants arrived to push him out of his family's hunting grounds. It is even more remarkable that some friendly Indians helped the Pilgrims appropriate Indian preserves. One of the first songs made in this country tells of the gentle Indian maiden who greeted the traveler from far away lands.

The Little Mohee

mus-ing, _____ my-self on the grass_____ Well, _ who should come by me, ___
fol-low, _____ you're wel-come to roam _____ To the hut in the clear-ing ___
loves me _____ and ev-er will be _____ More _ hon-est, and tru-er ____
by her, _____ she sat on the strand, _____ And the last time I saw her __

— but an In-di-an lass. _____ 2. She
— where-in I make my home." _____ 3. I
— than _ an-y Mo-hee." _____ 4. The
— she was wav-ing her hand. ___

5. But when I was home, then not a soul did I see
   That could even compare with the charm of Mohee.
   And the girl that I'd loved proved unfaithful to me,
   So I turned my ship backward to the land 'cross the sea.

6. And when I returned there, I found her once more,
   And she gave me her hand as I knelt on the shore.
   I said, "I am sorry, but I've come back to thee."
   And that is the story of my little Mohee.

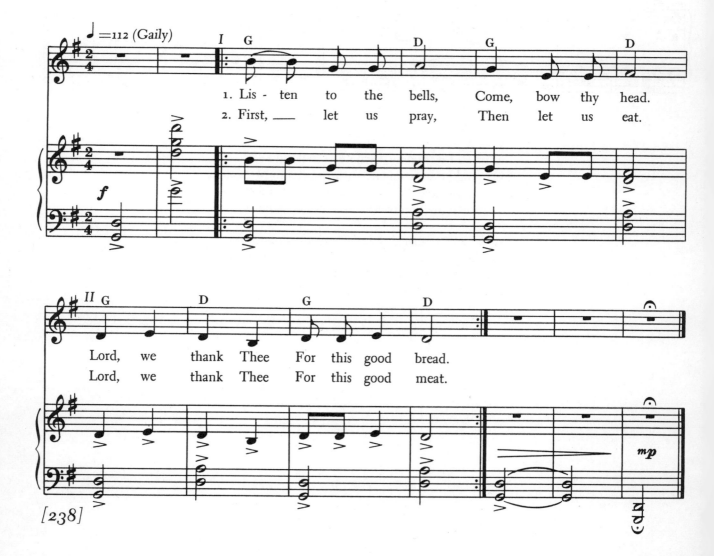

CANONS CAN BE fun to sing. Without our worrying about harmonies or intricate arrangements, we can sound like expert choristers when we join in singing canons. This canon should be special fun for Thanksgiving time because, if sung with care and rounded tones, it may sound like joyous bells ringing out holiday greetings. Omit the piano part when you perform this song as a canon.

Listen to the Bells

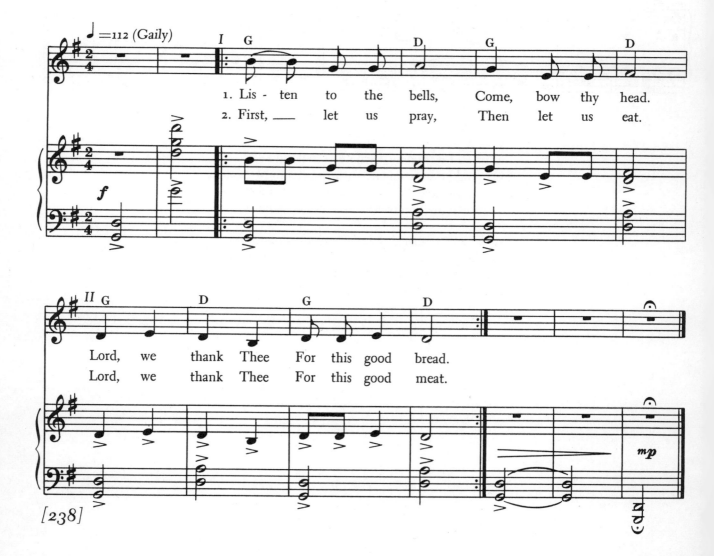

WINTER

As AUTUMN PASSES the days get shorter, the winds begin to blow a little colder, and the ant stores up provender while the grasshopper wastes his time enjoying himself. Nowadays, winter isn't so bad. Our homes are heated, stocked with cans and preserves, entertained by wireless radio and television, and accessible through publicly cleared highways. But in the days when many of our songs were made up, winter was a different time.

❧ HERE IS ONE of the songs of faith that reveals the fear which winter's onset brought to isolated communities. Valley dwellers feared avalanches and heavy snow falls, capable of destroying their homes. Farmers prayed that their barns contained enough feed to maintain their farm animals until spring. Often they wondered why the Lord had invented winter in the first place.

Winter Has Come

♩.=66 (Simply)

1. Win - ter has come up - on ___ our loved ones,
Chorus: Far - ther a - long, we'll know all a - bout it,

Leav - ing our homes so cheer - less and tried.
Far - ther a - long, we'll un - der - stand why.

Cheer up, my broth - ers,
Cheer up, my broth - ers,

think of   the spring - time; We'll un - der - stand   it   all   by   and by.
think of   the spring - time; We'll un - der - stand   it   all   by   and by.

last time

MODERN PAINTERS sometimes put down impressionistic generalities on canvas instead of striving for photographic likeness. This ridiculous song, with its impressionistic verses, feels more like winter to me than many songs which carefully describe the snow, the ice, and the dreary gray sky of our coldest season. All w's must be changed into v's, all frowns must be changed into smiles.

In the Vinter

1. In the vin - ter, in the vin - ter-time, Ven the vind blows on the vin-dow-panes, And the vim - men with the
2. In the vin - ter, in the vin - ter-time, Ven the snow comes vil - ly - nil - ly, And it vav - ers ver - y
3. In the vin - ter, in the vin - ter-time, Ven the vind vis - tles on the val - en-tines, Vich is vel - come to the

vest - coats Leave ___ vel - oc - i - pedes in the vest - i - bules. Ah,
von - der - ful, As ___ it vafts to the vest - vard. Ah,
vim - men - folks Vat is vork - ing in the vax - vorks. Ah,

Chorus

vim - men, ah, men, Ah, vim - men, ah, men.

1.

last time

1-5

DASHING THROUGH the snow in a one-horse open shay can be great fun if one is bundled in warm clothing. Otherwise, the fate of poor Charlotte may befall the careless adventurer who prefers blue lips and purple toes to the ordinary kind. Young men who complain that their loved ones are cold to them should congratulate themselves that their loved ones aren't frozen solid.

The Frozen Girl

1. Young Char - lotte lived on a moun - tain top, in a
   win - try night as the sun went down, a __
   daugh - ter, dear," her __ moth - er cried, "A __
   Charles, "The night is so pierc - ing cold, the __

bleak and lone - ly spot; There were no oth - er dwel - lings there, ex - cept her fa - ther's
mer - ry sleigh came by, Her lov - er's voice was heard out - side, and bright - ly shone her
blan - ket round you fold." "Oh, no, my silk - en cloak is warm, 'twill keep me from the
reins are hard to hold." And Char - lotte faint - ly an - swered, "Yes, I am ex - ceed - ing

cot, And yet on man - y a win - try night, young men would gath - er
eye. At the vil - lage fif - teen __ miles a - way, was to be a ball that
cold." Her bon - net and her __ gloves put on, she leaped in - to the
cold." He cracked his whip and he said, "The ice does gath - er on my

there, For her fa - ther kept a so - cial house, and she was wond-rous fair.
night, And though the air was pierc- ing cold, her heart was warm and light.
sleigh, And they swift- ly sped down the moun-tain-side, and o'er the hill a - way.
brow." And __ Char-lotte then more faint- ly cried, "I'm grow- ing warm-er now."

1.

last time

2. That
3. "Oh,
4. Said

5. Thus on they rode through the frosty air, and the glittering cold starlight,
Until at last the village lamps, and the ballroom came in sight.
They reached the door and Charles reached out, and gave his hand to her.
"Why sit you like a monument, that cannot move nor stir?"

6. He took her hand in his own and found, it was hard as any stone,
He tore the silk from off her face, and the cold stars on it shone.
Then slowly to the lighted hall, her lifeless form he bore,
Charlotte's eyes were closed for aye, her voice was heard no more.

[245]

CHRISTMAS AND HANUKKAH

◄§ IN OLDEN TIMES Christmas was celebrated on January 6th. Later the calendar was changed so that Christmas came on December 25th. Many people celebrate the twelve days of Christmas from the 25th of December to the 6th of January. And there are plenty of songs to carry them through because our Christmas song bag is almost as large as all our other song bags put together.

Practically all religions celebrate one of their favorite holidays at the end of the year. For the Romans it was Saturnalia, for the Jewish people it is Hanukkah, and for Americans of Christian faith it is the happy Christmas season.

CHRISTMAS IN AMERICA brings with it a Santa Claus on every corner. Department stores and railroad stations set out loud-speakers which broadcast traditional songs. Radio and television shows feature Christmas programs. Magazines have special Christmas issues. But one song is all we need for Christmas singing. And only one spirit need predominate for the holiday, the spirit of peace on earth to men of good will. This song may be performed as a three-part canon if the piano part is omitted.

Christmas is Coming

Christ-mas is com-ing, The goose is get-ting fat.

Please put a pen-ny In the old man's ___ hat;

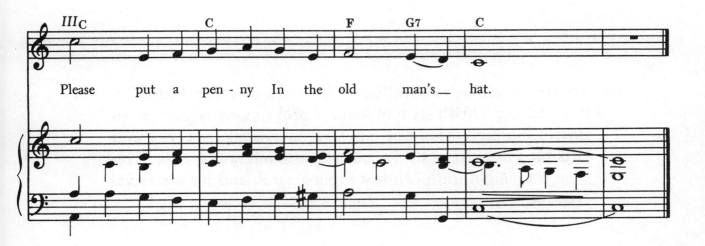

Please put a pen - ny In the old man's_ hat.

To THE GERMAN celebration of Yule we owe our Christmas tree and our Christmas tree songs. Carol singing is part of our British heritage. Many of our Christmas songs are welcome gifts presented to us by various other immigrant groups. This song is an eighteenth century French carol, and it's my secret favorite.

The Winter Season

1. The win - ter sea - son of the year, When to the
soon as to these hum - ble beasts Ap - peared His
love - ly sto - ry's still un - told, These hum - ble

world our Lord was born, The ox and don - key, so they say, Did keep His
face, so mild, so sweet, With joy, they knelt be - fore His grace, And gent - ly
beasts, so rough and rude, Through-out the night of ho - ly birth Drank no

Chorus

| d min. | a min. | E | a min. | G | | F | | C | | C | E | a min. |

ho - ly Pres - ence warm.
kissed His ti - ny feet. How man - y ox - en and don-keys you know, If they were
wa - ter, ate___ no food.

_mp_   _mf_

5 4 2

| a min. | a min. | E | F | G | | C | | a min. | a min. |

there, where first___ He came, How man - y ox - en and don-keys you know, At

_mp_

1

D E7 a min. E7 a min.

such a time, would do the same?___

1.   last time

2. As
3. Our

cresc.   _f_   _dim._   _mp_

❧ AMERICA'S SANTA CLAUS arrives after a chimney descent and fills the holiday stockings with sweets and toys. France's *Bonhomme Noël* leaves presents on the hearth. German immigrants began the custom of leaving gifts under the tree. Even our favorite Christmas tree song is translated from the German—"Oh, Tannenbaum." Pennsylvania Americans added new words to the old ones, and the singers must now act out the playing of the instruments without smiling.

I'll Play Something for You

♩ =144 (Ländler)

1. I'll

play some-thing for you. What will you play for me? I'll play for you the vi - o - lin:
play some-thing for you. What will you play for me? I'll play for you the clar - i - net:
play some-thing for you. What will you play for me? I'll play for you the sax - o - phone:
play some-thing for you. What will you play for me? I'll play for you the tym-pa - ni:

Repeat as necessary after 2nd verse

Fid- dle fi fi, fid- dle fi fi, Fid- dle fi fi, fid- dle fi fi.
Ep- ple bep- ple bep-ple, ep- ple bep-ple bep-ple, Ep-ple bep-ple bep-ple, ep- ple bep-ple bep-ple;
Schmet-ter enk trenk, schmet-ter enk trenk, Schmet-ter enk trenk, schmet-ter enk trenk;
Boo- roo- room boom, boo- roo- room boom, Boo-roo-room boom, boo- roo- room boom;

♩ =100 *(Pompous)*   a min.

Oh, Christ-mas tree, oh, Christ-mas tree, Your leaves are green for-

1.   last time
ev - er.   2. I'll
                  3. I'll ev - er.
                  4. I'll

5. I'll play something for you.   Schmetter enk trenk, schmetter enk trenk,
   What will you play for me?   Schmetter enk trenk, schmetter enk trenk;
   I'll play for you the piccolo: Epple bepple bepple, epple bepple bepple,
   Tweedle eedledeedle, tweedle eedledeedle,   Epple bepple bepple, epple bepple bepple;
   Tweedle eedledeedle, tweedle eedledeedle;   Fiddle fi fi, fiddle fi fi,
   Boorooroom boom, boorooroom boom,   Fiddle fi fi, fiddle fi fi.
   Boorooroom boom, boorooroom boom;   CHORUS

[253]

As the holiday season progresses, Christmas greetings give way to prayers and wishes for the new year. Our last song serves as a link between the old year and the new. It's an old English carol, and its wishes for you are our wishes.

We Wish You
A Merry Christmas

HANUKKAH, "The Feast of the Candles," is a Jewish holiday celebrated during the Christmas season. It commemorates the liberation of the Hebrew Temple by soldiers under the command of the great Hebrew general, Judah Maccabeus. We know many Hanukkah songs, but this song tells the historic meaning of the holiday.

Mi Y'malel

Mi Y'-ma- lel g'vu- rot Yis-ra- el O- tan mi yim- ne?

Hen b'-chol dor ya-kum ha-gi- bor Go -el ha - am.

Mi Y'-ma-lel g'vu-rot Yis-ra-el O-tan mi yim - ne?

Hen b'-chol dor ya - kum ha-gi-bor Go-el ha - am.

Sh'ma! Ba-ya-mim ha-hem ba-z'man ha - ze.

Ma-ka-bi mo-shi-a u-fo-de. U-v'ya-mey-nu kal am Yis-ra-

el.

Yit - a - ched ya - kum l' - hi - ga - el.

Stories are told by prophets of old,
When dangers threatened
Israel arose to scatter her foes
Throughout the land.

Ah . . .
When the foe besieged the Temple door
From our ranks came heroes as before.
Judah Maccabeus saved us then
So, today will Israel rise again.

INDEXES

INDEXES

INDEX OF SONGS

Index of Songs

UNCLE SAM'S FARM

INDEX OF FIRST LINES

Index of First Lines

Index of First Lines

YONDERS TREE

THE TYPE FACE used for the text of this book (and for this type note) is Caledonia, designed by W. A. Dwiggins for the Linotype machine. It is a contemporary letter of original design, though related in basic style to several eighteenth-century English type faces now called "transitional"—more regular in construction than "old style," but not so rigid, mechanical, and uncompromisingly vertical in stress as the "modern" types designed later. Caledonia was influenced in particular by a splendid type cut about 1790 for William Bulmer by William Martin, but its final modeling derives from the subtle and personal touch of the master calligrapher who drew it.

The lyrics under the music have been set in Electra, another of Mr. Dwiggins's Linotype faces. Electra is a wholly original design, not based on any historical model.

William Addison Dwiggins (1880-1956) was one of the most versatile and distinguished of contemporary American graphic artists. During the earlier part of his career he engaged chiefly in commercial art, lettering, and advertising typography. From the middle 1920's he devoted himself mainly to type designing and book typography, both with conspicuous success. His hobby was puppetry, in which he perfected a new system of counter-balancing string marionettes. His writings include a textbook on advertising typography which is a classic in its field, many cogent essays on book typography and type design, a monograph on the reform of the paper currency, two influential pamphlets on puppet construction, plays for his puppet theatre, and short stories. The American Institute of Graphic Arts awarded him its gold medal in 1929, and he was made an honorary M.A. by Harvard University in 1953.

The principal display type in the book is Perpetua, designed by the British artist Eric Gill (1882-1940). Perpetua is another original and contemporary type design without historical antecedents. Whereas the construction of types such as Caledonia and Electra shows the influence of the calligrapher, Perpetua's shapes basically derive from stone-cutting, a form of lettering in which Gill was eminent. The subordinate display type is Bulmer italic, a modern copy of the type face by William Martin that was the germinal influence on Caledonia.

The music has been handwritten throughout by MAXWELL WEANER. *The type was set by* THE COMPOSING ROOM, INC., *New York. The book was printed in photo-offset by* AFFILIATED LITHOGRAPHERS, INC., *New York. It was bound by* H. WOLFF, *New York. The typography and design is by* CHARLES FARRELL.